PLANT-BASED KETO MEAL PLAN

A KICK-START GUIDE FOR YOUR HEALTH, ATHLETIC PERFORMANCE, MUSCLE GROWTH AND WEIGHT LOSS. RECIPES TO STREAMLINE YOUR VEGAN LIFESTYLE WITH A 28 DAYS DIET PLAN.

GINA LARSEN

CONTENTS

INTRODUCTION

Keto diets have really come on strong in the past year and a half and for good reason. It's a great way to not only shed those unwanted pounds **q**uick, but also a great way to get healthy and stay that way. For those that have tried the Keto Diet and are still on it, it's more than just a diet. It's a way of life, a completely new lifestyle. But like any major shift in our lives it is not an easy one, it takes an incredible amount of commitment and determination.

Good for Some But not for all? - Although a ketogenic diet has been used to greatly improve people's **q**uality of life, there are some out there who do not share the majority's way of thinking. But why is that exactly? Ever since we can remember we have been taught that the only way to get rid of the extra weight was to quit eating the fat filled foods that we are so accustomed to eating every day. So instructing people to eat healthy fats (The key word is Healthy) you can certainly understand why some people would be skeptical as to how and why you would eat more fat to achieve weight lost and achieve it fast. This concept goes against everything we have ever known about weight loss.

How Keto Started - Discovered by endocrinologist Rollin Woodyatt in 1921 when he found that 3 water -soluble compounds Aceture, B-hydroxybutyrate and Acetoacetate (Known together as Ketone bodies) were produced by the liver as a result of starvation or if the person followed a diet rich with high fat and very low carbs. Later on that year a man from the Mayo Clinic by the name of Russel Wilder named it the "Keto-genic Diet," and used it to treat epilepsy in young children with great success. But because of advancements in medicine it was replaced.

My Struggles Starting Keto - I started Keto February 28th 2018, I had made an attempt at the Keto Diet once before about 6 months prior but was never able to make it through the first week. The first week on Keto is the worst part of the entire process, this is when the dreaded Keto Flu appears also called the carb flu. The Keto Flu is a natural reaction your body undergoes when switching from burning glucose (sugar) as energy to burning fat instead. Many people who have gone on the Keto Diet say that it actually feels similar to withdrawing from an addictive substance. This can last anywhere between 3 days to an entire week, it only lasted a few days in my case.

People who have had the keto Flu report feeling drowsy, achy, nauseous, dizzy and have terrible migraines among other things. The first week is usually when people attempting a Keto Diet fail and quit, just remember that this happens to everyone early in the process and if you can get past the first week the hardest part is over. There are a few remedies you can use to help you get through this rough spell. Taking Electrolyte supplements, staying hydrated, drinking bone broth, eating more meat and getting plenty of sleep. Keto Flu is an unfortunate event that occurs to everyone as the body expels the typical day-to-day diet. You just have to power through.

What Does A Ketogenic Diet Look Like? - When the average person eats a meal rich in carbs, their body takes those carbs and converts them into glucose for fuel. Glucose is the body's main source of fuel when carbs are present in the body, on a Keto diet there are very low if any at all carbs consumed which forces the body to utilize other forms of energy to keep the body functioning properly. This is where healthy fats come into play, with the absence of carbs the liver takes fatty acids in the body and converts them into ketone bodies.

An ideal Keto diet should consist of:

- 70-80% Fat
- 20-25% Protein
- 5-10% Carbs

You should not be eating more than 20g of carbs per day to maintain the typical Ketogenic diet. I personally ate less than 10g per day for a more drastic experience but I achieved my initial goals and then some. I lost 28 lbs. in a little under 3 weeks.

What Is Ketosis? - When the body is fueled completely by fat it enters a state called "Ketosis," which is a natural state for the body. After all of the sugars and unhealthy fats have been removed from the body during the first couple of weeks, the body is now free run on healthy fats. Ketosis has many potential bene-fits-related to rapid weight loss, health or performance. In certain situations like type 1 diabetes excessive ketosis can become extremely dangerous, where as in certain cases paired with inter-mittent fasting can be extremely beneficial for people suffering from type 2 diabetes. Substantial work is being conducted on this topic by Dr. Jason Fung M.D. (Nephrologist) of the Intensive Dietary Management Program.

What I Can and Can't Eat - For someone new to Keto it can be very challenging to stick to a low-carb diet, even though fat is the cornerstone of this diet you should not be eating any and all kinds of fat. Healthy fats are essential, but what is healthy fat you might ask. Healthy fats would consist of grass-fed meats, (lamb, beef, goat, venison), wild caught fish and seafood, pastured pork & poultry's. Eggs and salt free butters can also be ingested. Be sure to stay away from starchy vegetables, fruit, and grains. Processed foods are in no way accepted in any shape or form on the Ketogenic diet, artificial sweeteners and milk can also pose a serious issue.

ZUCCHINI RAVIOLI: A LOW CARB VEGAN MEAL

Your favorite comfort food with a healthy twist! This vegan zucchini ravioli smothered with marinara and creamy Alfredo sauce is the ultimate of low carb vegan recipes.

Vegan zucchini ravioli covered in tomato and cream sauce and topped with basil and parmesan

But not all satisfying meals have to make you bloat post consumption. Which is why I created these vegan zucchini ravioli. A low carb vegan meal like no other.

People get so wrapped up in diet fads, they often forget that eating is supposed to be amazing.

I am usually what is called a carb maniac, I love my carbs and my body craves them. But from time to time, I feel the need to have a carb vacay. However salad doesn't usually cut it for me.

WHAT CAN I MAKE FOR DINNER THAT IS LOW CARB?

Glad you asked! As I was looking for more low carb vegan recipes (did you see this one yet?), I got inspired to make these vegan zucchini ravioli. Little pockets of tightly wound thin zucchini slices filled with a basil and spinach ricotta to die for, and topped with flavorful tomato sauce, creamy Alfredo.

The cherry on the top (or the cheesy topping) is buttery hemp seed pine nut parmesan. I bakes to a borderline crisp and is so good, you'll almost forget you're not actually eating pasta. Almost.

Hemp seeds are my favorite dirty little secret. Tiny pockets of whole food fat filled with protein. They are rich in essential nutrients, and also provide dietary fiber. They make a perfect plus one with our fabulous butter friend, the pine nut.

This yummy combo first appeard in my Scalloped Cauliflower recipe. I mixed them with breadcrumbs to form a perfect crispy topping. So I thought I'd give it a try as the cheesy sub to these bad boys here too. Side note: You can also make this grateable parmesan cheese.

HOW TO MAKE ZUCCHINI RAVIOLI?

Vegan zucchini ravioli may seem like a pain, but they are actually quite simple.

Make ricotta filling. Hand holding glass jar filled with vegan spinach nut based ricotta

Slice the zucchini into strips, fill and fold. Step by step folding of zucchini ravioli filled with vegan spinach ricotta

Bake. Zucchini ravioli covered in red and white sauce on a while plate.

TRICKS TO MAKING THESE EVEN EASIER

The key to successful dinners is to cut corners. Yep, I am telling you to cheat. No one ever said survival is truthful all the time, so go with it.

Skip the alfredo or use store bought.

Use your favorite jarred tomato sauce.

Make the ricotta ahead of time, heck double the batch and freeze for next time!

Slice the zucchini the day before and keep in the fridge until ready.

You should always have some vegan Parmesan on hand, so that's a no brainer.

HOW TO MAKE THIS VEGAN RAVIOLI KID FRIENDLY

Because I am an advocate in making one meal work for everyone, here is how I have had less mean looks at my table:

Serve the ravioli as is over pasta.

Cut up the ravioli and mix in with pasta.

Serve ravioli in parts in a kid build your own pasta bar. Blanch the zucchini strips by putting them in the bottom of the pasta strainer and draining the hot pasta over it. Then serve the sauces and ricotta separately and let kids build their pasta bowls themselves. My kids have control issues so this always helps.

Play with your food! Put everything out on the table and let the littles make their own zucchini pockets. You can even add more fillings and let them decide what to put in.

PS- If you want to make this meal low fat too, sub the ricotta for the cauliflower ricotta in this recipe!

By the way, if you are stuck in a dinner rut and need some help there, I have a comprehensive FREE guide on weekly meal planning that comes with a **FREE** 3 day meal plan and shopping list! Join here!

- Prep Time: 25 mins
- Cook Time: 35 mins
- Total Time: 1 hr
- Servings: 6

Your favorite comfort food with a healthy twist! This vegan zucchini ravioli smothered with marinara and creamy Alfredo sauce is the ultimate of low carb vegan recipes.

Ingredients

- 4 zucchini (medium sized)
- 1 cup raw cashews
- 1 cup walnuts
- 4 cloves garlic
- ½ - 1 teaspoon sea salt (depends on red sauce used)
- ¼ teaspoon ground black pepper
- 1 cup water
- 1 cup fresh basil
- 1 cup fresh spinach

Hemp Pine Nut Parmesan:

- ¼ cup hemp seeds
- ¼ cup pine nuts
- ¼ - ½ teaspoon sea salt (see note)

Toppings:

- Easy Tomato Marinara
- or Crockpot Red Sauce
- Cream Sauce (use sauce portion only)
- or Creamy Alfredo (use sauce portion only)
- US Customary - Metric

Instructions

If you're making your own marinara, make now and set it to cook while prepping the rest of the meal.

If you haven't made Alfredo make it as well, follow the directions in the link.

Make parmesan by adding all ingredients to a food processor and blending until you get a nice crumble.

Preheat oven to 350 degrees F (175 C).

Slice zucchini lengthwise into very thin strips. A mandolin slicer will give you the best results but you can also do it with a sharp knife and some patience! You can throw away the very edge pieces as those are all skin. You should have about 15 thin slices per zucchini.

Place slices on paper towels and sprinkle a little salt on them to help draw out some of the water. Let them sit while you make ricotta.

Place cashews, walnuts, garlic, salt, pepper, water, basil and spinach into a food processor. Pulse until you get a ricotta like texture. You want it slightly chunky, on the verge of pureed.

Wipe of the excess water and salt from the zucchini strips. Take two strips at a time and make an X.

Place a spoonful of ricotta mixture in the middle where the slices cross.

Then fold the tips of each slice into the middle one by one (see photo in post) to make a ravioli like pocket. Place them into a 9 x 12 baking dish.

Once all ravioli are made, drizzle both marinara and Alfredo over the ravioli. You can put as much or as little as you prefer.

Sprinkle with Hemp Pine Nut parmesan.

Bake for 35 - 40 minutes, until zucchini is fully cooked. Allow to set about 5-10 minutes after baking. Serve while still nice and warm!

Recipe Notes

This makes a total of about 30 ravioli. Each serving is 5 ravioli.

You can add all basil or all spinach if you prefer, just up to 2 cups of whatever one you do.

Adjust the salt for both the ricotta and parmesan to your liking. It all depends on the amount of salt used in the other parts of the recipe.

If you don't have pine nuts, you can always sub walnuts, although it won't have that same deep buttery flavor.

To make this even easier, you can always use a jarred marinara sauce and skip the creamy Alfredo, but it's highly recommended to make your own of both!

If you want to use the ricotta as a topping for something, use less liquid to make it thicker and more stable. Start with only a few tablespoons of water and add more to get the texture you like.

You can also sub the ricotta for this low fat version

Nutrition Facts

- Calories 360
- Calories from Fat 270
- Fat 30g46%
- Saturated Fat 3g15%
- Sodium 310mg13%
- Potassium 650mg19%
- Carbohydrates 15g5%
- Fiber 3g12%
- Sugar 5g6%
- Protein 12g24%

2

FLUFFY LOW CARB KETO ZUCCHINI BREAD PANCAKES (PALEO, VEGAN)

Easy fuffy low carb zucchini bread pancakes made with coconut flour and almond flour. These keto friendly flourless pancakes are a sneaky way to add shredded zucchini- You won't even know it's in there! Vegan, Paleo, Gluten Free.

When it comes to my favorite healthy breakfasts, thick and fluffy pancakes take first place. In the past few weeks, we've seen low carb cinnamon roll pancakes and healthy pancakes with banana. It is now time to go a little seasonal, with zucchini season in full swing!

Adding shredded zucchini to these thick fluffy pancakes make them taste exactly like zucchini bread, especially with a sprinkling of mini chocolate chips throughout. I promise you won't taste them (as evidenced by these flourless zucchini fudge brownies) and they give you a veggie boost!

On its own, coconut flour required significantly more liquid to produce even remotely edible pancakes. On the other hand, almond meal worked okay but tasted gritty. By combining the two, it produced almost diner-like pancakes, but so much healthier and completely sugar free!

How to make pancakes thick and fluffy

To key to making pancakes ultra fluffy and pillow-like, is to be patient. I know its easy for us to want pancakes right there and then but trust me on this- It is well worth the wait!

It is best to use a good quality non-stick pan. Even though it is non-stick, I would recommend spraying a tiny bit of cooking spray or coconut oil over it. Heat the pan on low-medium heat, and for the duration of the cooking process, do not exceed this.

Once the pan is hot enough, add your batter and immediately cover the pan with a lid. This ensures the pancakes are cooked evenly and also the even heat distribution aids the pancakes rising and puffing up.

When the edges start to go golden brown, simply flip and repeat the process!

Easy! While eggs are necessary for the keto pancakes recipe, they aren't for the fluffy flourless pancakes made with almond milk and vinegar.

It might sound a little odd to use vinegar, but this is what is needed to replace the egg AND yield perfect fluffy pancakes. When combined with the baking powder, it produces a rising capability which you'd assume would only be feasible by using eggs.

If you don't have vinegar on hand, you can use lemon or lime juice, but the results won't be 100% the same. Also, be sure to use a good quality blender to ensure the batter is evenly combined.

Tips and Tricks for a perfect pancake-

Allow the batter to sit for at least 10 minutes before cooking

If the batter is too thick, add a little extra liquid. If the batter is too thin, add extra almond flour (keto version) or rolled oats (flourless vegan version).

Cook smaller pancakes- Quicker cooking time but easier to flip

Do not over-cook! Pancakes continue to 'bake' while cooling down!

Squeeze the excess liquid out of the zucchini (using a dishcloth or paper towel works great)!

Easy fuffy low carb zucchini bread pancakes made with coconut flour and almond flour. These keto friendly flourless pancakes are a sneaky way to add shredded zucchini- You won't even know it's in there! Vegan, Paleo, Gluten Free.

- Prep Time: 10 minutes
- Cook Time: 5 minutes
- Total Time: 15 minutes
- Servings: 3

Ingredients

Keto Low Carb Pancakes (Keto, Paleo, Sugar Free, Dairy Free, Grain Free)

- 1/2 cup almond flour
- 2 tbsp coconut flour
- 1-2 tbsp granulated sweetener of choice
- 1/2 tsp baking powder
- 1 tsp cinnamon

- 1/4 cup shredded zucchini
- 3 large eggs
- 1/4 cup milk of choice coconut milk, almond milk etc
- 1-2 tbsp chocolate chips of choice Optional

Flourless Egg Free Pancakes (Vegan, Gluten Free, Sugar Free, Dairy Free)

- 1 heaping cup rolled oats Can sub for quinoa flakes
- 1 tsp baking powder
- 1/2 cup unsweetened applesauce
- 1 tbsp apple cider vinegar
- 1 tbsp sticky sweetener of choice maple syrup or agave works best
- 1 tsp cinnamon
- 1/4 cup shredded zucchini
- 1/4-1/2 cup liquid of choice almond milk, coconut milk etc.
- 1-2 tbsp chocolate chips of choice Optional

Instructions

In a high-speed blender, combine all your ingredients and blend until just combined. The batter should be thick and pourable.

Allow the batter to sit for 10 minutes. Just before cooking, stir in chocolate chips is desired.

On low-medium heat, preheat a non-stick pan. It would be best to coat with a little bit of oil. Once hot, pour small portions of the batter into the heated pan. Cover immediately, and cook for 2-3 minutes, or until the edges are golden brown. Flip and repeat.

Notes

If the batter is too thin, add more almond flour (keto version) or rolled oats (flourless version).

Fluffy Low Carb Keto Zucchini Bread Pancakes (Paleo,

Vegan) can be batch cooked- simply allow to cool before freezing/refrigerating.

Nutrition

Serving: 1serving | Calories: 125kcal | Carbohydrates: 3.5g | Protein: 7g | Fat: 7g | Fiber: 3g | Vitamin A: 200IU | Vitamin C: 1.7mg | Calcium: 40mg | Iron: 0.5mg | NET CARBS: 1g

3

FRUITLESS GREEN SMOOTHIE BOWL {VEGAN, LOW CARB, SUGAR FREE}

Reduce your sugar intake with this fruitless green smoothie bowl. It will energize you without a sugar crash afterward. It's gluten free, dairy free, vegan, and free from refined sugar.

The green smoothie has become *q*uite the popular breakfast staple over the last few years. I'm all for healthy greens playing a starring role in people's lives. The problem is all of the other ingredients that people layer in that end up skyrocketing the sugar levels of what used to be a healthy breakfast. That's why I'm bringing you a fruitless green smoothie bowl recipe today.

Too much sugar, even the healthy kind in fruit, can cause

imbalances in the body. The fructose sends insulin levels high, and guess which direction they go after that? Yup, crashing down.

No fruit green smoothie bowl

All that sugar can be tough on your digestion as well. Without proper digestion, you're not going to absorb all of those great nutrients that you're trying to ingest.

Kyo Green sprout blend smoothie.jpg

Kyo-Green went ahead and created a special organic sprouts blend for your digestion with goodies like *q*uinoa, lentils, flax, broccoli, sunflower, and pumpkin.

Smoothie bowl without fruit

They didn't stop there. They also included a great greens blend with barley grass, wheat grass, brown rice, FOS from chicory root, and chlorella. Even if you don't know how to pronounce some of those words, you should just know that these ingredients all provide good prebiotics to help your digestion work its magic with ease. Happy digestion equals happy body.

Fruitless smoothie bowl

I decided on this fruitless green smoothie bowl instead of a straight up drink because I know that some people like to chew. Chewing can also lead to a better feeling of satiety.

Often times when you drink a smoothie, you still feel hungry at the end. When you're eating out of a bowl and chewing some crunchy toppers, your mind and body both get with the program that you're having a proper meal instead of just a drink.

No fruit green smoothie.jpg

Oh, and the crunchy toppers are also half the fun. You get more healthy fat and protein with my choices of coconut, hemp, and sesame seeds. Feel free to mix and match your favorite nuts and seeds.

And because you've kept your smoothie bowl fruit free, you could go a little crazy and throw a berry or two on top. That'll still be a lot less sugar than if you blended bananas and dates in the smoothie. You'll also get some natural sweetness to balance out some of the greens.

- Prep Time: 10 minutes
- Total Time: 10 minutes
- Servings: 1 bowl

Ingredients

- 2 tsp chia seeds
- 1/2 cup coconut milk or water (carton, not canned)
- 1 cup zucchini, copped (ideally frozen)
- 1/2 cup cucumber, chopped
- 1 handful baby spinach
- 1 scoop vanilla protein powder (I like Sunwarrior Warrior Blend)
- 1/4 tsp ground cinnamon
- 2-3 tsp almond butter (or any variety)
- 1 tsp maca powder (optional)
- Granola, muesli, or banana (to provide carbs)
- Chopped nuts and/or seeds (to provide crunch and fats)
- Berries, cacao nibs, bee pollen, etc. (for toppings)

Instructions

Pop the chia seeds into a glass or mug and pour over the coconut milk/coconut water, then give it a little stir. Allow to sit for 5 to 10 minutes to allow the chia seeds to absorb some of the liquid and form a gel.

Place all other smoothie ingredients into the jug of your blender. Pour over the chia gel mix.

Blend until you have a thick, creamy smoothie. If your blender won't pulse, add in a splash more liquid just to get it going (you can use more coconut milk/water or just add water).

Scoop the smoothie in to a bowl and top with some crunchy, chewy carbohydrates, seeds and whatever else you like.

Notes

*for a nut-free version of this smoothie bowl, simply replace the nut butter with some coconut butter or a seed butter e.g. pumpkin seed butter, tahini, etc. It will still be absolutely delicious!

Nutrition Per Serving (1 of 2 bowls)

Calories: 310 Fat: 15.6g Saturated fat: 1.9g Sodium: 171mg Carbohydrates: 41.5g Fiber: 9.5g Sugar: 19g Protein: 7.9g

4

HEARTY SEED BREAD

Before we talk about this hearty seed bread, also known as the best vegan keto bread. We should talk about the what and the why. Like what is keto? And why would anyone eat a keto diet?

The gist of the ketogenic diet, or keto for short, is that it uses fat to burn fat. When you eat a high fat and low carbohydrate diet your body works through the elimination of glucose. However, when glucose levels are cut off due to low-carb eating, the body starts to burn fat instead and produces ketones that can be measured in the blood. When your body begins to produce enough ketones, you will be in a state of ketosis.

A ketogenic diet has been around for decades and was originally recommended to patients living with epilepsy. But it has now gained popularity for its potential weight-loss benefits. However, it's *q*uite notable to mention, and for many reasons, I do not eat a keto diet.

I did experiment with it for a little while. And while I did feel more consistent energy levels and appetite, keto wasn't sustainable or desirable long term for me. I love vegetables and fruits and grains way too much.

I mean, I've built my entire career around them. But vegetables, and especially fruits and grains are high in carbs and not recommended on the keto diet. And I cannot imagine a life where I have to keep those foods in moderation. Keto diet did lead me to a few new discoveries in the kitchen though. Like this vegan keto bread.

The best vegan keto bread on the internet.

It's true – I promise you this is the best vegan keto bread on the internet. Most vegan keto bread recipes are nutritionally void, full of dairy and taste eggy. They are not great.

So, I wanted to create my own keto bread where the nutrients are the stars. This seeded bread is based off of Sarah's hearty life-changing loaf. The structure and density are the same, but the main ingredients differ greatly because this version is free of oats.

This vegan keto bread is made entirely from seeds. It is free of gluten, grains, nuts, dairy, eggs, soy and sugar. And it is loaded with selenium, magnesium, phosphorus, folate, zinc, and vitamins B1, B2, B3 and B6.

And if you're counting, the macros per slice are: 2 grams net carbs, 6 grams fat, 8 grams fiber and 7 grams protein.

- Yield: 16 Slices
- Prep Time: 10 Minutes
- Cook Time: 1 Hour
- Total Time: 1 Hour 10 Minutes

Hearty vegan keto bread made entirely of seeds. Free of gluten, grains, nuts, dairy, eggs, soy and sugar. Full of fiber, phytonutrients and healthy fat.

Ingredients

- 1 1/2 cups raw pumpkin seeds (divided)
- 1/2 cup psyllium husks (whole)
- 1 cup raw sunflower seeds
- 1/2 cup flax seeds
- 1/2 cup chia seeds
- 1 teaspoon fine sea salt
- 1 tablespoon maple syrup or pinch powdered stevia
- 3 tablespoons olive oil
- 1 1/2 cups warm filtered water

Instructions

Preheat the oven to 350 degrees and line a 1-pound loaf pan with parchment paper and set it aside.

Pulse 1 cup of the pumpkin seeds in a food processor or blender until finely chopped. It should be medium-coarse flour consistency (as shown in the images).

In a large mixing bowl combine the pumpkin seed flour with the remaining pumpkin seeds, psyllium husks, sunflower seeds, flax seeds, chia seeds, salt and maple syrup (or stevia).

Then stir in the warm water and olive oil, and combine until your batter forms.

With your hands press the batter into the loaf pan and bake for 45 minutes.

Take the loaf pan out of the oven and remove the loaf. Put the loaf on a sheet pan so the top is down and return it to the oven to bake for 15 minutes.

The bread is done when you tap on it and it sounds hollow inside.

Cool completely and then slice into 16 pieces.

Serve toasted.

Notes

STORAGE: If you will consume this loaf within a week, store it in the refrigerator. For longer store it in the freezer. For the best texture and taste, toast each slice before enjoying (either from the refrigerator or from frozen).

TIPS: This bread requires no proofing. Maple syrup or honey (1 tablespoon) can be subbed in place of stevia. Melted coconut oil can be subbed in place of olive oil.

Nutrition Per Serving (1 of 2 bowls)

MACROS (per slice): 2g net carbs, 6g fat, 8g fiber, 7g protein

5

BULLETPROOF HOT CHOCOLATE {LOW CARB, KETO, GLUTEN FREE, DAIRY FREE, VEGAN}

Yes, you can still enjoy your favorite seasonal drink even while watching your carbs! This comforting Bulletproof Hot Chocolate is sugar free, low carb and packed with healthy fats!

This Bulletproof Hot Chocolate will be your favorite winter drink! Low carb, keto, paleo & gluten free too. From Lauren Kelly Nutrition

This Bulletproof Hot Chocolate will be your favorite winter drink! Low carb, keto, paleo & gluten free too. From Lauren Kelly Nutrition

If you aren't familiar with Bulletproof Hot Chocolate, Coffee or Tea, basically it's adding healthy fats (like grass fed butter, ghee or coconut oil) to your preferred beverage.

It's said to help keep you full and provide you with a bunch of energy. I personally love to add MCT oil to my tea every morning. Many people drink Bulletproof Coffee or Tea instead of eating breakfast, but I have to eat something in the morning. That's just me.

If you are also wondering what in the world MCT oil is... here ya go...

MCT oil is made up of Medium Chain Fatty Acids that are considered easily digestible and beneficial fats. Instead of being metabolized through digestion like most other foods, these fats are processed in the liver.

MCTs provide fast and lasting energy and are easily absorbed by the body, according to Wellness Mama. You can read more about it here.

This Bulletproof Hot Chocolate will be your favorite winter drink! Low carb, keto, paleo & gluten free too. From Lauren Kelly Nutrition

So for this recipe, I've made it with both MCT oil (which is tasteless) and coconut oil and I liked the MCT oil better, but that's mainly because I don't like coconut!

This Bulletproof Hot Chocolate will be your favorite winter drink! Low carb, keto, paleo & gluten free too. From Lauren Kelly Nutrition

And by blending this all up in the blender it gets thick, creamy and frothy! Who doesn't love frothy??

I know many of you make bulletproof coffee, but since I don't drink coffee, this is my thing. I am sure I can make a bulletproof tea...doesn't that sound delicious? Maybe that will be my next recipe!

The healthy fats in this definitely keep you full for a while. And that is the whole premises of the ketogenic/low carb diet. Your body is burning fats instead of carbohydrates for energy. These healthy fats genuinely keep you full for so long so you are no longer hungry every few hours.

And many people have this misguided notion that you are always hungry for carbs and sugar. That's just it, once you cut them out of your diet you no longer crave them.

It's been over 3 years since my last intestinal surgery and I am hoping this lifestyle will prevent it from happening again. Eating a low carb diet helps reduce inflammation in your body and that's exactly what I am hoping for.

And let's not forget the sugar free treats (like this Bulletproof Hot Chocolate) on occasion. It reminds me that I can still enjoy a sweet (sugar free) cookie, brownie or whatever I like. That doesn't sound that restrictive, am I right?

This Bulletproof Hot Chocolate will be your favorite winter drink! Low carb, keto, paleo & gluten free too. From Lauren Kelly Nutrition

Let me know if you have changed your diet and lifestyle and what small goals you are hoping to achieve! I love hearing what everyone's goals and aspirations are, especially when they deal with health and wellness.

Remember, small changes make a HUGE difference.

Also let me know if you have any questions or comments on cutting down on carbs from your diet. It's easier than you think. And yes, it completely sustainable.

And no, I do not think you should eliminate carbs at all. I actually don't believe anyone should eliminate entire food groups from your diet (unless there is a food allergy or sensitivity). I am strictly talking about reducing complex carbs and processed foods.

- Prep Time: 10 minutes

- Total Time: 10 minutes
- Servings: 1 cup

Thanks for stopping by! Bets of luck with your future goals!

Ingredients

- 1/2 cup hot water (not scolding hot) (I heat mine in a small saucepan on the stove)
- 1/2 cup unsweetened almond milk
- 2 tablespoons coconut oil or MCT oil
- 2 tablespoons unsweetened cocoa powder
- 1/4 teaspoon vanilla
- 1-2 teaspoons Erythritol
- Heavy whipping cream optional

Instructions

Place all of the ingredients in a blender and blend until smooth.

Top with Heavy Whipping Cream if desired.

IMPORTANT: Be very careful when opening a high speed blender with a hot liquid, as it may create a vacuum. Make sure water isn't scalding hot. Blend it only for a few seconds at a time, allowing the pressure to release every time.

Nutrition Facts

- Servings: 1
- Amount per serving
- Calories 282
- % Daily Value*
- Total Fat 30.4g 39%
- Saturated Fat 24.6g 123%
- Cholesterol 0mg 0%
- Sodium 96mg 4%
- Total Carbohydrate 8.2g 4%
- Dietary Fiber 4.1g 15%

- Total Sugars 2.3g
- Protein 2.6g
- Vitamin D 1mcg 3%
- Calcium 168mg 13%
- Iron 2mg 10%
- Potassium 262mg 6%

6

KETO TOFU SCRAMBLE

I've been hearing a lot about Ketogenic diets for a while now, but I never really dove in to see what all the fuss was about. Friends have lost weight and said how good they feel eating Keto, so I was intrigued when this new book came my way: The Ketogenic Mediterranean Diet: A Low-Carb Approach to the Fresh-and-Delicious, Heart-Smart Lifestyle

The book, by Robert Santos-Prowse, is part nutritional/metabolic lesson, Keto crash course, and recipe book. It's really perfect for anyone that wants to learn more since it's like three books in one. I really like the section that lays it all out... what can I eat, what I can't eat. Of course it goes into more detail for each of those sections, but it's a handy little guide to peek at as you learn the Keto lifestyle. And, if you really need to get additional meal ideas, there is a meal plan toward the back of the book!

The Tofu Scramble recipe was a good start for my family to try (as we are mostly vegetarian), so it's nice to know what Keto options there are for us. (It's not as full of the healthy fats as some of the other recipes, but just add a few slices of avocado and that would do the trick nicely!) My hubby loved it and asked for the recipe so he can make it if I'm not home.

The ingredients are clean and simple. All the herbs came from my garden and, if you've been reading my blog for a while, you know I'm going to preach to you about how easy it is to grow your own herbs! Can I get an amen?

A little secret to crisping up tofu is to get out as much moisture as possible. Wrap it in paper towels and put something heavy on top – a cast iron skillet perhaps or, in my case, sharpening stones.

Add the tofu to a skillet with heated oil and cook until lightly browned. Add the seasoning slurry and nutritional yeast and stir together. Take off heat and add in the garlic, scallion, and herbs – cooking with residual heat for one minute.

Besides the time needed to drain the tofu, this was a super quick recipe that I think could be served at any time of day. This Keto Tofu Scramble dish is also a Vegan Tofu Scramble!

- Serves: 2
- Cooking Time: 10 minutes

Ingredients

- 1 package extra firm tofu, drained
- 2 Tbs olive oil
- 1 tsp turmeric
- 1 tsp ground cumin
- 1/2 tsp smoked paprika (or regular, if that's all you have)
- 1/2 tsp course salt

- 1 tsp ground black pepper
- 2 cloves garlic, chopped
- 2 Tbs water (I used four)
- 2 Tbs nutritional yeast
- 1 Tbs fresh sage, julienned
- 2 Tbs fresh basil, julienned
- 1 Tbs fresh rosemary, finely chopped
- 1 scallion, diced
- 1 avocado, sliced (optional)

Instructions

1. To drain the tofu, wrap it in paper towels and place a heavy weight on it, replacing the towels when necessary
2. While draining tofu, julienne the sage and basil, and chop the rosemary, garlic, and scallion
3. In a small bowl, combine the turmeric, cumin, paprika, salt, pepper, and water; mix and set aside
4. When the tofu is drained, cut into half inch cubes
5. Heat the oil in a skillet over medium heat
6. Add the tofu and sauté, stirring frequently until all sides are lightly browned
7. Add the spice slurry and stir to coat
8. Add in the nutritional yeast
9. Cook until sauce achieves a sticky consistency (add more water at this stage if necessary)
10. Remove the pan from heat and add in the sage, basil, rosemary, garlic, and scallion; stir
11. Allow to cook with residual heat of the pan for one minute
12. Serve

NOTES: Use organic, locally sourced ingredients whenever possible

Nutrition

Calories: 417kcal | Carbohydrates: 42g | Protein: 25g | Fat: 17g | Saturated Fat: 3g | Cholesterol: 13mg | Sodium: 990mg | Potassium: 1152mg | Fiber: 8g | Sugar: 11g | Vitamin A: 1680IU | Vitamin C: 43.1mg | Calcium: 455mg | Iron: 4.3mg

7

ROASTED POBLANO PESTO ZOODLES {LOW CARB}

Pesto zoodles with roasted poblanos are a light, tasty take on pesto pasta. A low carb, gluten-free, vegetarian recipe to make for an easy weeknight dinner. There's a vegan option, too! With arugula, poblano peppers, basil, and cilantro, this pesto has some zippy heat and incredible summery taste.

You see, I've been on a fresh, light food kick for a few weeks now. Well, minus the barbecue gluten-free meatloaf. But I think it's about time to shed some of that winter worry and get back to what matters – family, and good, fresh, healthy food. Am I right?

Maybe now that the husband is coming home I should try to lay off the cookie dough for a while. If you missed that confession, just check out my behind-the-scenes post on Instagram. Haha!

And just in time for all that light, fresh spring food comes my friend Jessica Merchant's (How Sweet Eats) new cookbook, The Pretty Dish. Just from the cover, it's stunning. I mean, WOW! Bright, beautiful, happy photography and totally DELICIOUS food!

Of course, I went straight for the poblano pesto zoodles because I'm on a HUGE pesto kick. Um, just wait till next week and you'll see why. Anyways, this sounded outrageously good and GAH, it sure delivered. With a little heat from the poblanos and an infusion of herby flavor from arugula, basil, and cilantro, it tasted fresh, summery, and a little zippy.

On a side note, this pesto zoodles recipes happens to be one of the most made recipes on Pretty Dish so far!

The Pretty Dish is one of those cookbooks full of healthy comfort foods. There's a lot packed in, so you'll always find something to make. By the way, that hummus is soooo amazing! Oatmeal station? Yup, Jessica's on it. She's also got a DIY beauty section, and I'm eyeing the face scrub recipe. Believe me, there's MORE. The Pretty Dish has a little of everything you'd want in a cook-book. It's FUN, pretty, and healthy – what more could you ask for?

And, just to encourage any pesto-haters, you'll want to give this poblano pesto recipe a try. I have a friend who is a pesto-hater, seriously, and she totally fell in LOVE when I made her the pesto zoodles.

Just in case you like it when I get all nutritional nerdy on you, this pesto pasta is loaded with vitamin C and powerful antioxidants. So go make this AMAZING pesto, you will love it, too!

Ingredients in this Pesto Zoodles recipe:

Made with simple Ingredients you probably already have ...

- Poblano Peppers
- Olive oil
- Parmesan (Vegans sub with Nutritional Yeast)
- Basil
- Argula
- Salt and pepper
- Lemon
- Garlic

Making roasted Poblano pesto in a food processor homemade spicy pesto in a food processor

Plus you can use it in more than just zoodles. Maybe poblano pesto potato salad should be made next. Thoughts? Um, yes!

- Prep Time: 5
- Cook Time: 15
- Total Time: 20 minutes
- Yield: 2

Roasted Poblano Pesto Zoodles are a light, tasty take on pesto pasta, perfect for a spring or summer meal. A low carb, gluten-free, vegetarian dish to make for an easy weeknight dinner.

Ingredients

Poblano Pesto:

- 2 poblano peppers
- 1/2 cup fresh arugula
- 1/2 cup fresh basil
- 1/4 cup fresh cilantro

- 1/4 cup grated Parmesan cheese (Or Nutritional Yeast for Vegan option)
- 1/4 teaspoon salt
- 1/4 teaspoon ground black pepper
- 3 tablespoon olive oil

Zoodles

- 2 medium zucchini squash
- 2 tablespoons olive oil
- 1 tablespoon unsalted butter
- 2 cloves garlic, minced
- Pinch of crushed red pepper flakes
- Juice of 1/2 lemon
- Torn fresh basil, for topping
- Grated Parmesan cheese, for topping (Nutritional Yeast for Vegan option)

Instructions

To Make the Poblano Pesto:

To roast the poblano peppers, preheat your oven's broiler.

Remove the core and seeds from the peppers and slice into pieces. Lay the pieces on a baking sheet. Broil skin side up for about 10 minutes, or until the skins are completely charred and black. Broiling time can vary, so check every 2 minutes or so. Immediately remove the peppers from the oven and use kitchen tongs to quickly place them in a resealable plastic bag. Seal the bag and set aside for 20 to 30 minutes, or until softened.

Remove the peppers from the bag. Peel off and discard the skin. It's okay if a little bit of char remains as it adds to the flavor.

In a food processor, combine the peppers, arugula, basil, cilantro, Parmesan, salt and black pepper. Process until the mixture is combined, then stream in the olive oil with the processor running.

To Make the Zoodles:

Spiralize the zucchini into noodles.

In a large skillet, heat the olive oil and butter over medium-low heat. Add the garlic and red pepper flakes and cook for 1 minute, then stir in the lemon juice. Add the zoodles and toss well to coat.

Cook, tossing often, for 5 to 6 minutes, or until the zoodles soften slightly. Add in the poblano pesto and toss well. Cook for 5 minutes, or until warmed.

Serve immediately with basil and Parmesan cheese (or nutritional yeast).

NOTES

Vegan option: Replace the parmesan in the pesto with nutritional yeast

Tip: If you're just getting into zucchini noodles, try combining them with gluten-free pasta. Use half regular gluten free pasta, half zucchini noodles, and toss. It's a great way to incorporate more veggies and lighten up the meal.

Nutrition Per Serving

Calories: 487 Fat: 14g Saturated fat: 2.3g Sodium: 365mg Carbohydrates: 75g Fiber: 10g Sugar: 4g Protein: 14g

8

MEXICAN-SPICED KETO CHOCOLATE

Keto chocolate is high in fat and sugar free for a low carb twist, but all you'll taste is smooth, silky dark chocolate flavor coupled with a pungent spice mix that is sure to warm you up a little! It's so easy to make chocolate at home with just a few ingredients. Try it and see for yourself!

But if the last two months of health, family, work, and home-related curveballs has taught me anything, it's:

(1) never set a blogging schedule, because that's just an invitation for it to be blown to bits by the universe

and

(2) be flexible!

So, the long and short of it is that I am going to have a lot of chocolate recipes for you in March and April. Do you mind? Nah, I didn't think you would.

Great! Let's kick off with Mexican-spiced Keto chocolate.

BACK UP: WHAT'S KETO?

Ah ok, good question. In short, Keto is a diet that emphasizes high fat intake, coupled with moderate protein and low carbs (or net carbs). (Side note: I tried to find a good link to explain the diet in an unbiased way, but I can't find one. If anyone has any good resources that explain keto without trying to either convert you or terrify you, please share them!)

Mexican Spiced Keto Chocolate (low carb, paleo, gluten free, sugar free)

At first, I was a little wary of the keto diet because it seemed kind of gimmicky (mostly because 99% of the recipes out there were called "fat bombs"... which sounds disgusting). But, I stand corrected, mostly because I learned a little bit more about Keto and realized many of my recipes already fit the bill.

Like Paleo, I was already following the keto diet somewhat by listening to my body, but I just didn't know it. And since I've stopped nursing and stopped craving as many carbs, I've started to want to eat more low carb foods again.

So, you'll see a few keto recipes (and other low carb recipes) popping up here, but please don't be put off by them. Like all of my gluten free treats, they don't make it to the blog unless they're good. Not "good for keto". Just good. You with me? Awesome.

A NEW AND IMPROVED KETO CHOCOLATE RECIPE

As a result, I revisited a low carb chocolate recipe I already had on my site (I used to call this Mexican spiced sugar free chocolate, in case you're wondering why it looks slightly familiar). The old recipe calls for coconut oil, which I know a lot of you liked because it is easy to find these days. Most grocery stores carry coconut oil, and you can always find it online.

GINA LARSEN

However, the drawback to using coconut oil as the base here is that you must keep your keto chocolate refrigerated; at room temperature, the chocolate starts to melt and get pretty messy. It's not fun to eat, and it's impossible to take this chocolate with you anywhere, or bake with it (which makes sense, since we're all bakers! I get tons of questions about using this, and the original sugar free dark chocolate recipe that you can find here, in your gluten free baking).

Ok, if I'm being really honest here, there were a couple of things I wanted to change. First, the consistency because, as I mentioned above, the meltiness just wasn't cutting it. I knew the base would have to consist of cocoa powder and some fat that was solid at room temperature, and a solid fat that isn't terrible for you isn't the easiest to come by.

The solution was so obvious, if you know how any chocolate is made: cacao butter. It's the base of all chocolate, and by mixing it with my favorite cocoa powder, I created a chocolate that holds its shape and consistency at room temp. Woo! The one drawback is that cacao butter isn't as easy to find as coconut oil, but you can find it online. I got mine on Amazon. Or, you can use coconut oil, but you'll be right back where we started with the melting problem. If you don't mind, I don't.

But cocoa powder + cacao butter = a chocolate that appeals to absolutely no one's sweet tooth. So, the next hurdle was the sweetener. The original version of this recipe used granulated stevia, but if you weren't using the same brand as I did, the chocolate, once it firmed up, could become gritty. I never want to send you on a wild goose chase for precise brands of low carb sweetener, so I swapped the sweetener in this new version of the recipe for liquid stevia.

The rest of the recipe is still pretty similar to the original, although I adjusted the amount of spices and vanilla extract slightly. But you won't see anything too shocking, and it's all still pantry ingredients.

MAKING KETO CHOCOLATE

This recipe takes very little time to make, and it's all prep time. You do not need to cook anything, although you will have to melt the cacao butter (or coconut oil, if you're using it instead), which you can do in the microwave or over a double boiler. Then just stir in the remaining ingredients, pour into your chocolate mold, and ... wait. The waiting is probably the hardest part.

Once the chocolate has set, you can eat it, or bake with it!

Mexican Spiced Keto Chocolate (low carb, paleo, gluten free, sugar free)

You can mold the chocolate into any shape you want. Just buy whatever mold best suits your needs (again, I get all my chocolate molds on Amazon; you can also check baking supply stores. This is the one I use [aff. link]). Just know that, of course, your yield will probably vary when you use a different mold.

If you'd like to use it in place of unsweetened bakers chocolate, simply leave out the stevia.

If you're planning to use this chocolate in cookies, you can swap it in for commercial sugar free chocolate with one notable exception: since this keto chocolate doesn't contain any additives or stabilizers to help it hold its shape, you'll need to compensate as much as possible for its tendency to melt in the oven. That means keep it as cold as possible before baking, and chop it (or mold it) larger than the pieces you'd like to see in the baked cookie. Ideally, you'd chop the chocolate, and put it in the freezer, then fold it into the dough immediately before forming the dough into balls and baking. Or, just do the best you can to keep the chocolate cold, and chop it to a size that looks too large.

Do not try to bake with this if you are using coconut oil as the base.

Feel free to leave out the spices if you just want traditional chocolate flavor.

These tiny chocolates pack a punch of flavor that will bring you back to life. They are so dark-chocolatey that they taste almost coffee-ish, and they are sweetened just enough to take the bitter edge off the cocoa powder, but not a drop more. Start with that, and mix in some spicy magic: cinnamon, nutmeg and chili powder. Ohhhhh, the chili powder. You see, when you mix it all up, you might think "gosh I am disappointed that these flavors are so weak." Just wait.

Just as the liquid mixture transforms to a solid as it chills, so too do the drab, washed out spice flavors transform into an amalgam of flavor that evolves from sweet to pleasantly bitter and finishes with a just-bold-enough smoky spiciness from the cinnamon and, more so, the chili powder that will send a shiver down your spine in the best possible way.

- Yield: 18 Pieces
- Prep Time: 10 Minutes
- Total Time: 10 Minutes

Keto chocolate is high in fat and sugar free for a low carb twist, but all you'll taste is smooth, silky dark chocolate flavor coupled with a pungent spice mix that is sure to warm you up a little! It's so easy to make chocolate at home with just a few ingredients. Try it and see for yourself!

Ingredients

- 1/2 cup cocoa powder
- 1/2 teaspoon chili powder
- 1/4 teaspoon cinnamon
- 1/8 teaspoon nutmeg
- 1 pinch black pepper
- 1 pinch fine sea salt
- 50 grams cacao butter, (about 1/4 cup when melted)
- 1/4 teaspoon vanilla extract
- 25 drops liquid stevia, or monk fruit (to taste)

Instructions

- In a small mixing bowl, whisk together the dry ingredients (cocoa powder through salt). Set aside.

- Add the cacao butter to a microwave-safe bowl and heat on high in 30 second increments (stirring in between) until melted. You can also melt in a double boiler, if you prefer.
- Stir the vanilla and stevia into the melted cacao butter.
- Add the cacao butter mixture to the cocoa powder mixture and stir until smooth.
- Divide between two lightly greased mini loaf pans or a lightly greased chocolate mold (here is the mold I used for these chocolates, and I also have this heart mold).
- Allow it to set at room temperature until firm.
- Store in an airtight container at room temperature for up to 5 days, or in the freezer for up to 3 months.

NOTES

Make sure you're using a the best *q*uality cocoa powder you can find, since this is the primary source of flavor in these chocolates.

Also be sure you're using spices that aren't too old. I tried this with chili powder that had been in my cabinet for over a year, and newly purchase chili powder and the flavor difference was substantial.

For a little more complex flavor, replace half of the cinnamon with pumpkin pie spice.

Check that you're using food grade cacao butter. If you can't, or don't want to, get cacao butter, you can use coconut oil instead. But, if coconut oil is the bast, you must keep the chocolates refrigerated until just before eating, and you can't bake with them.

Although it is not mandatory, it is helpful to have a silicone candy mold for this. They are *q*uite inexpensive, and you can use them over and over again for chocolate or even gummies. This is the one I used for these.

You can mold the chocolate into any shape you want. Just buy whatever mold best suits your needs (again, I get all my chocolate molds on Amazon; you can also check baking supply stores. This is the one use. Just know that, of course, your yield will probably vary when you use a different mold.

If you'd like to use it in place of unsweetened bakers chocolate, simply leave out the stevia.

If you're planning to use this chocolate in cookies, you can swap it in for commercial sugar free chocolate with one notable exception: since this keto chocolate doesn't contain any additives or stabilizers to help it hold its shape, you'll need to compensate as much as possible for its tendency to melt in the oven. That means keep it as cold as possible before baking, and chop it (or mold it) larger than the pieces you'd like to see in the baked cookie. Ideally, you'd chop the chocolate, and put it in the freezer, then fold it into the dough immediately before forming the dough into balls and baking. Or, just do the best you can to keep the chocolate cold, and chop it to a size that looks too large.

Do not try to bake with this if you are using coconut oil as the base.

Feel free to leave out the spices if you just want traditional chocolate flavor.

Nutrition Information:

Amount Per Serving: CALORIES: 40 TOTAL FAT: 3g SATURATED FAT: 2g TRANS FAT: 0g UNSATURATED FAT: 1g CHOLESTEROL: 0mg SODIUM: 10mg CARBOHYDRATES: 6g FIBER: 1g SUGAR: 1g PROTEIN: 1g

9

SHIRATAKI NOODLES WITH ALMOND BUTTER SAUCE(VEGAN + PALEO)

Have you tried Shirataki noodles before? They're often called "Miracle" noodles or "Zero" noodles because of the fact they contain no calories, fat or carbs! Sounds too good to be true, right? They're naturally gluten-free and grain-free, meaning they are also suitable for Paleo diets.

Suffice to say, they're often used by people trying to lose

weight and make an excellent alternative to wheat or rice-based noodles.

I decided to use them to create a classic peanut noodle style dish. To make it paleo-friendly I used almond butter instead of peanut and coconut aminos instead of soy sauce.

It later dawned on me that mange tout peas aren't paleo-friendly (doh!) as a big part of the diet is "no legumes" so if you're here for a paleo recipe – please ignore those peas you see in the photos!!

The perfectionist in me was tempted to make the meal again without them but the lazy girl in me insists it's fine. I might update the photos next time I make it... But anyway, you can of course use whichever vegetables you want!

So how does it taste? I had heard mixed reviews about the shirataki noodles and their texture but I found them absolutely delicious!

They are slightly more chewy but it's not at all unpleasant, in fact I loved it and would happily eat these instead of wheat or rice noodles any day.

Coconut aminos do an amazing job at creating a soy sauce flavour without containing any soy and the almond butter could almost be mistaken for peanut butter in this dish, especially when mixed with the rest of the ingredients. You could also use cashew butter or tahini.

So all in all, you've got a healthy, vegan & paleo-friendly dish that tastes just like a classic peanut noodle stir fry. Delicious!

Not only is this dish so healthy but it's SO easy too and can be ready in under 10 minutes! That's always a good thing. You simply need to stir fry the veg, add the noodles and the rest of the ingredients to make a sauce.

One pan, minimal washing up, ready in a flash and all for under 200 calories. It's a dream come true...

This noodle dish is:

- Vegetarian & vegan

- Gluten-free & paleo-friendly
- Dairy-free & eggless
- Low calorie (only 190 calories for a very generous serving!)
- One-pan (minimal washing up)

Ready in under 10 minutes and SO easy to make

- Yield: 1
- Prep Time: 2 Minutes
- Cook Time: 8 Minutes
- Total Time: 10 Minutes

A delicious dinner that's easy, healthy and both vegan and paleo-friendly! Feel free to use whichever veg you wish. Mushroom and peppers would also work really well.

Ingredients

- 1 tbsp mild olive oil or coconut oil
- 2 cloves garlic, minced
- 3 spring onions, diced
- 100 g long-stemmed broccoli
- 1 small carrot, cut into small batons
- 1/4 cabbage, shredded
- 1 pack, g Shirataki noodles*
- 1 tbsp almond butter
- 1 or 2 tsp sriracha sauce, depending on how spicy you want it
- 2 tbsp coconut aminos**

Instructions

Heat the olive oil in a wok or large saucepan on a medium heat and add the garlic and onions. Cook for a couple of minutes until softened, then add the rest of the veg.

Whilst the vegetables are cooking, prepare your shirataki

noodles by emptying them out of the packet and rinsing them well with warm water. Add them in with the vegetables.

Once everything is just about cooked, add the almond butter, sriracha and coconut aminos. Stir into the vegetables and noodles to create a sauce and warm through.

Serve and enjoy!

Notes

*You can often find shirataki noodles in health food stores. They are usually called either "zero" or "miracle" noodles. You can also buy them online.

**Coconut aminos can be found in health food stores or online. If you're not avoiding soy, you can use equal amounts of soy sauce or tamari sauce (gluten-free).

Nutrition Information

- Calories 190
- Carbohydrates 19.3g
- Fiber 7.9g
- Protein 8.1g

10

LOW-CARB NOODLE BOWLS WITH CREAMY CURRY SAUCE (NUT-FREE, DAIRY-FREE, PALEO, VEGAN + KETO)

A low-carb, keto noodle bowl bursting with fresh, crunchy vegetables and agar-based low-carb, keto noodles. Smothered in a creamy (dairy-free!), keto curry sauce. The keto sauce is so good, I call it "curry crack sauce". Addicted... hard.

Guide on how to start keto.

Keto shopping lists, recipes, and more! Start keto with this FREE 5-step guide.

What are they? Low-carb, keto noodles! Only... they're not your average soy-infested low-carb, keto noodle.

Low-Carb Noodle Bowls with Curry Sauce #lowcarb #keto #hflc #lchf #paleo #primal #glutenfree

These keto Dry Kanten Noodles are made with agar, a compound extracted from seaweed. Often used as a vegan alternative to gelatin. Asian cultures use agar to naturally suppress appetite and assist in weight loss. Additionally, agar is used to normalize blood sugar, treat diabetes and constipation. Consisting of a gel-like polysaccharide, agar bulks up in the gut to stimulate the intestines giving us the feeling a fullness, leading to less consumption and more elimination.

Agar contains no sugar, no carbs (it has an equal amount of carb to fiber, so it is completely net carb neutral), with a touch of calcium and iron. By binding with toxins throughout the digestive process, it efficiently moves toxic waste out of the body. Other benefits associated with agar is its ability to reduce

- Easier to cook: no boiling, draining or rinsing
- Neutral taste
- Not as crunchy
- Soy-free
- Preservative-free
- They're naturally gluten-free, safe for vegans, keto peeps and kids love them, too.

My experience preparing these keto Kanten Noodles for the first time... was uneventful, really. Place in bowl, add hot water, soak, drain, eat. One thing I did notice is that they have a slight seaweed smell to them when they're soaking. But the smell went away after preparing and doesn't transfer to the taste of the final keto noodle whatsoever. Just a heads up.

Health note...

If you are following a low-FODMAP eating style, I'm not comfortable recommending that you eat Kanten noodles, or natural seaweed products of any kind. Can't do the keto noodles?

Check the notes of this keto recipe for an outline of what to do instead.

However, if you have had success with using seaweed to normalize your hypothyroid condition, these noodles are your friend! Rather than taking iodine in its straight form, many of my thyroid clients add natural seaweed products like keto Kanten Noodles to their daily rotation.

If your gut is happy, seaweed products (and these delicious noodles) are one more tasty tool that you can add to your low-carb, keto resource kit.

- Prep time: 10 mins
- Cook time: 5 mins
- Total time: 15 mins
- Serves: 4

Low-carb, keto noodle bowl bursting with fresh, crunchy vegetables and agar-based low-carb noodles. Smothered in a creamy (dairy-free!) curry sauce.

Ingredients

- Noodle Bowl
- 16g, 1 full pack of Kanten Noodles
- 2 carrots, julienned
- ½ head cauliflower, roughly chopped
- 1 red bell pepper, diced
- handful fresh cilantro, chopped
- 2 handfuls mixed greens
- Creamy Curry Sauce
- ¼ cup tahini or avocado oil mayo
- 2 tablespoons avocado oil or MCT oil
- ¼ cup water
- 2 tablespoons apple cider vinegar
- 2 teaspoons curry powder (I used my homemade curry powder)
- 1½ teaspoons ground coriander

- 1 teaspoon sea salt
- 1 teaspoon ground turmeric
- 1 teaspoon ground cumin
- ½ teaspoon ground black pepper
- ¼ teaspoon ground ginger

Instructions

Prepare Kanten Noodles by placing the two sheets of noodles in a large bowl. Lightly heat a couple of cups of water, a couple of degrees below boiling. Think: hot water that you can drink. Pour water over noodles and set aside while you prepare the rest of the ingredients. After about 5 minutes of soaking, strain and set aside in a large bowl to cool.

Add carrots, cauliflower, bell pepper and cilantro to the bowl with the noodles. Set mixed greens on 2 separate servings plates as the "base" to your meal.

Then, add all of the Curry Sauce ingredients to the jug of your high-powered blender and blend until smooth. Pour over the vegetable and noodle mixture and toss to coat.

Serve immediately or place in the fridge to cool for a couple of hours. Store in an air-tight container in the fridge for up to 2 days.

Notes

Protein boost: I served this with a grilled steak on the side. Feel free to use anything here. If you're low-carb or keto, add an animal protein. If you're vegan, try roasted chickpeas or tempeh.

Sesame-free: If you're allergic to sesame or just not doing seeds, make this keto recipe with avocado oil mayo. Or, make your own mayonaise. Using mayo would make this keto recipe unsafe for vegans and those with egg allergy/sensitivity.

Noodles: if you don't have a couple of packs of Kanten Noodles in your pantry just yet, you could make this recipe with zucchini noodles.

Nutrition Information Per Serving

- Calories: 192

- Calories from Fat: 138.6
- Total Fat: 15.4 g
- Saturated Fat: 2.1 g
- Sodium: 523 mg
- Carbs: 17.7 g
- Dietary Fiber: 10.4 g
- Net Carbs: 7.3 g
- Sugars: 3.9 g
- Protein: 4.3 g

11

INSTANT PALEO ICE CREAM (VEGAN, LOW CARB)

This dairy-free, sugar-free, low carb ice cream is creamy, full of antioxidants, and satisfys those ice cream cravings. It's also ready in an instant!

If you have been following me over the years, you will have seen quite a few of my favorite slow churn ice cream recipes on www.bettyrawker.com, (the Cherry Garcia and Mint Chocolate Chip have been the biggest hits!) but the wonderful thing about this recipe, is there is no ice cream machine needed! All you need is a blender. Yep, its that simple. I use my Vitamix to whip this right up in less then a minute, and I don't see why it wouldn't also work in a standard blender? I bet a food processor would also work! Though if you are looking for an excuse to finally buy a Vitamix, this is the perfect reason!

The consistency of this ice cream is more like a soft serve, and kinda like a nice creamy sherbet, and the optional MCT oil adds more of a "whipped" and lighter texture. You can make it with or without the MCT. I added the option of adding the MCT oil for those who are looking for ways to add more brain fuel & high energy oil into their diet, as this is the perfect recipe for it. I am currently only "flirting" with a keto diet, not following it as strictly as many do, but I can say I am enjoying the increased fats in my diet, along with eating lower carb, yet still totally natural treats.

To get a firmer consistency for the photos, I simply put the ice cream into a bowl, then stuck it into the freezer for about 30 minutes after blending, then scooped into into the bowls. Just don't freeze it too long, as it will get hard if frozen for a few hours. If you want to make a large batch of ice cream that freezes well, try my slow churn recipes on bettyrawker.com that include a splash of vodka. Honestly, I usually just enjoy this ice cream right out of the blender. I really like this recipe for it's simplicity. After a long day, it's the perfect afternoon snack to whip up in a blender. Bam, instant ice cream sundae, just top with this magic shell!

Before you ask, "Can I use something other than coconut milk?" I will at least say, this recipe also worked with my homemade walnut milk. And I made my husband a blueberry ice cream using 1/2 cup of goat kefir + 1 cup frozen blueberries and that worked great, but since I am dairy free, I stick to coconut milk. I think the reason this instant ice cream works so well is because the coconut milk is high in fat, and when that creamy fat hits the frozen berries, it creams them right up.

- Prep Time: 10 minutes
- Total Time: 10 minutes
- Servings: 1 cup

Ingredients

2 cups FROZEN berries of your choice: strawberries blueberries, cherries

1/2 cup coconut milk full fat, add slowly, as needed

1 Tablespoon MCT oil optional

1/4 teaspoon 1/4 vanilla extract omit for AIP

1 t optiona sweetener, if needed to taste I personally don't add any

Instructions

Add 1 cup of frozen berries/fruit to your blender.

Pour in 1/2 cup coconut milk, then blend. You may need to stop and start the blender a few times to push the "ice cream" down from the sides. Try not to over blend, as you want to keep this cool, thick & creamy.

Once fruit and coconut milk is well combined, you have the option of blending in 1 Tablespoon of MCT oil. Pour in, the quickly blend a little longer.

Spoon dessert into an ice cream dish. (For the scoops of ice cream in the photos, I set the ice cream in the freezer for about 30 minutes to firm up, but this is totally not necessary, I usually just eat it right after blending)

Optional: Top with my instant magic shell recipe and freeze dried berries, and/or chopped nuts.

Nutrition Info

219 calories, 17 grams of fat, 14 total carbs, (11 net carbs), 2 grams protein.

12

GRAIN FREE LOW CARB KETO GRANOLA

This Grain Free Low Carb Keto Granola is SO crispy and crunchy! You'll never guess it's secretly healthy, gluten free and sugar free and paleo and vegan friendly!

Coconut Cashew Low Carb Keto Granola - SO crispy and crunchy that you'll never guess it's secretly healthy, low carb, gluten and sugar free and paleo and vegan friendly! The perfect breakfast or snack that's great for meal prep!

Liiiiike, the kind that doesn't cut the inside of your MOUTH OPEN.

Really. What did we ever do to granola that it would be so mean as to rip open our insides as we unsuspectingly munch through it, trusting that it has our best interests at HEART?

NOPE. IT DOES NOT.

It's ALMOST as bad as Captain Crunch. <– Don't lie. You KNOW that you know the exact cereal-mouth-pain that I am talking about.

Anyway. This low carb granola recipe is NOT that kind of granola.

It's crispy and CRUNCHY, like a deconstructed sugar free keto low carb granola bars recipe, or a bowl of homemade keto low carb cereal, yet not sharp and OUCHY. It's perfectly sweet and CLUSTERY-Y, yet is totally SUGAR FREE and GRAIN FREE.

Yeuuuuup. Granola without grains is a really thing that exists in your hungry-morning-breakfast-eater life and this sugar free granola recipe proves that it's JUST AS DELICIOUS.

Unlike a typical granola recipe, that boasts a mega load of oats, T-H-I-S grain free low carb keto granola uses NUTS and SEEDS to give it that addicting, CRAVE-ABLE CRUNCH that any normal, granola-eating person expects when they stack it HIGH on their morning bowl of Greek yogurt. It's kind of like no oats paleo oatmeal, but even LOWER carb!

Your inner texture freak is SRSLY not gonna know that ANYTHING is awry and that no oatmeal was used in the making of this sugar free granola recipe.

Punchy, flavorful coconut flakes, heart-healthy, roasty cashews and almonds, crunchy, good-for-your-gut chia seeds and a nourishing swirl of creamy coconut oil jive along to the breakfast beat, mixing and mingling with the flax egg and baking up to golden-brown, roasty yumminess, in a way that is going to make you RLY RLY excited to be eating nuts and seeds. AKA: BIRD FOOD.

The "flax egg" is the secret weapon to getting this keto

granola to form those coveted big, CRUNCHY, clustery pieces of magic. It helps everything stick together JUUUUST so.

Real life talk: do you really trust granola that doesn't have clusters? Exactly. You do not.

Make SURE you push a few pieces together during the bake-stir-bake-stir-bake-stir (annoying? Yes. Necessary? Very.) situation that the recipe calls for. This will ENSURE you cluster SUCCESS.

Insider secret for winning the "crunchy granola" championship: put the granola into the refrigerator once it's cooked. This hardens the coconut oil leading to hitting the crispy MOTHERLOAD. <– You don't have to keep it stored in the fridge for ever and ever. Just until the coconut oil does it thang.

Things to note: the inner part of my soul that loves chocolate RLLLLY wanted to mix some chocolate chips in (post baking, of course) but, due to many of you doing the "sugar free" thang, I quieted that voice.

If that is not you, that suggestion comes HIGHLY, well, SUGGESTED.

But, if you are a sugar-free person and chose to forgo the chocolate, we can still be internet BFFs.

- Prep time: 20 m
- Cook Time: 30 m
- Servings: 11

Ingredients

- 2 tablespoons Flax Meal
- 5 tablespoons Warm Water
- 2 tablespoons Monkfruit Sweetener, plus 2 teaspoons
- 2 tablespoons Coconut Oil, at room temperature, should be the consistency of softened butter
- 1 cup Raw Cashew Halves, 140 grams
- 1 cup Whole Raw Almonds, roughly chopped, 135 grams

- 1/2 cup Unsweetened Coconut Flakes, packed, 32 grams
- 2 tablespoons Chia Seeds, 20 grams
- 2 teaspoons Pure Vanilla Extract
- 1/2 teaspoon Sea Salt

Directions

Preheat your oven to 350°F and line a baking sheet with parchment paper or a silpat.

Place the flax meal in a large bowl and whisk in the warm water. Place into the refrigerator for at least 15 minutes so the flax meal can begin to gel up and thicken.

Once the flax has chilled, add in the monkfruit and coconut oil and stir together. The coconut oil won't mix in smoothly and will start forming small chunks, that is normal.

Add in all the remaining ingredients and stir until the flax/water mixture coats everything.

Spread evenly into one layer on the baking sheet. Bake 10 minutes, then stir. While stirring, trying to kind of stick a few pieces together so that they bake into chunks (if you like chunky granola. If not, don't worry about doing this.)

Bake another 10 minutes and repeat.

Finally bake another 5 minutes and then check for done-ness. You want the granola to be VERY golden brown when it's done cooking, although it won't feel crunchy yet. This could take another 5-15 minutes, so watch it in the last few minutes of baking.

Once done, let cool to room temperature on the pan. Then, transfer to an air-tight container and place into the fridge to cool and crunch up completely!

DEVOUR

Notes: Once chilled in the refrigerator, you can store the granola at room temperature as it will main it's crunchiness.

Nutrition facts

- Calories 199.8

- Total fat 17.4g
- Saturated fat 6.6g
- Polyunsaturated fat 1.8g
- Monounsaturated fat 4.0g
- Cholesterol 0.0mg
- Sodium 106.7mg
- Potassium 93.2mg
- Total carbohydrate 7.2g
- Dietary fiber 3.5g
- Sugars 1.5g
- Protein 6.2g

13

CREAMY, 2 MINUTE GOLDEN GODDESS DRESSING {VEGAN, GLUTEN FREE, KETO & PALEO FRIENDLY}

What a whirlwind these last few weeks have been!

With our super exciting, very much needed, last minute/spontaneous family vaycay underway, so much has happened in such a short period of time my head is seriously spinning!

We have traveled – flown, driven, walked – so far (SO FAR!!!) in such a short period of time, done, seen and eaten so much and have just been having THE best time but my head . . . won't stop spinning!

Coconut (or Greek style yogurt) is infused with a sprinkling of garlic, touch of turmeric, a hint of ginger and a cheeky pinch of salt and pepper. Then we add a zesty squeeze of lemon juice to help lighten things up and cut through the richness of that creamy, aromatic base and um . . .

You guys . . .

This dressing?!

It's deliciously creamy, seriously, dreamy and packed with so much flavor that it may just knock your socks right off!

It's great on salads, it's great on burgers, it would be amazing drizzled over these roasted carrots, or these garlic roasted Brussels sprouts or even these crisp and crunchy baby taters too but it's also great simply slathered onto some fresh cut veggies (carrots, mushrooms and snap peas are my fave) but cucumber, broccoli, capsicum/peppers are all good too – you name it, it just works!

And you guys, this dressing – could not be any easier to make!

It's all natural made with just a handful of ingredients that I bet you have on hand already , it comes together in one bowl, in less than 2 minutes with no fancy blenders or specialist equipment required!

It comes together in one bowl, in less than 2 minutes and also happens to be vegan, gluten free, dairy free, keto, paleo friendly and 100% whole 30 complaint so everybody wins!

You guys, this dressing . . . it's insanely deliciously, I'm talking seriously addicting, and something you are going to want to slather, drizzle and eat on allllll of the things!!

All natural, quick and easy, light,fresh, creamy, dreamy, anti-inflammatory, gloriously golden, dairy free dressing . . .

Makes approx 1 cup of all natural, quick and easy, creamy, dreamy, garlic infused, gloriously golden dressing

Ingredients

- 1 cup coconut or Greek style yogurt
- 1 teaspoon garlic powder
- 1/4 teaspoon turmeric
- 1 pinch of ground ginger

- 1 teaspoon of freshly squeeze lemon juice (approx 1/3 of a medium sized lemon)
- 1 teaspoon of salt
- 1/4 teaspoon of freshly ground black pepper

Optional add ins;

- 2 scoops of Vital proteins unflavored collagen peptides
- 1 teaspoon of Meadow and Marrow Bone Broth Concentrate – for an extra boost of protein and gut healing goodness
- 1 Tablespoon of MCT oil – brain boosting energy

Method –

1 – Place all ingredients into a small bowl and stir until well combined.

2 – Taste and adjust seasonings to taste. Also, if you prefer a thinner consistency add a touch of coconut or almond milk (or milk of choice) a teaspoon at a time to reach desired consistency.

3 – Drizzle over your favorite salad, roasted veg, carrot and zucchini fritters or use it to simply dip fresh cut veggie sticks for a seriously flavorful snack.

4 – Store in an air-tight container in the fridge and should keep well for up to 7 days but I doubt it will last that long, mine never does.

Nutrition

- Calories: 84
- Sodium: 130.8 mg
- Fat: 8.1 g
- Saturated Fat: 1.1 g
- Unsaturated Fat: 6.6 g
- Carbohydrates: 2.7 g
- Protein: 1.6 g

14

KETO GREEN SMOOTHIE

A low-carb high fat Keto Smoothie to snack on or to have for breakfast! No sugary fruit, no sweeteners, only low carb veggies, high fat avocado and ginger, lemon and cilantro for that special flavor!

A vibrantly green Keto Smoothie in a glass.

Who knew creating keto smoothie recipes was about the

hardest thing ever?! Mostly, I felt is was easy to create keto diet recipes until now, but sweets and smoothies? Not so much.

The fact that the keto diet is mostly fruit-free and only allows a couple berries and that any sort of sugar, even a natural one like honey, is a big no no, makes creating a yummy smoothie super hard.

Let's be real here for a second. I'm not a huge fan of smoothies made with too many vegetables. I looove vegetables, don't get me wrong. My whole diet and blog and life's work revolves around vegetables. Both, raw and cooked. In smoothies and juices, however, ugh. Not so convinced. I prefer a delicious fruit smoothie without yogurt for example.

Adding oil to a smoothie can be a smart idea, especially great oils like MCT, it does taste kinda oily then though and not so smooth.

Mostly, smoothness in smoothies is acquired by adding banana which is the highest carb fruit ever so no bueno.

The smoothness in this keto green smoothie comes from…..*drumrolls please*…..avocado!!! The best fruit ever on the planet.

An extremely healthy fat and absolutely delicious! I love to use frozen avocado for this Keto Avocado Smoothie because 1. I don't have to plan ahead and always have ripe avocados on hand and 2. It gives me an ice cold smoothie.

And just in case you were wondering. No, it doesn't brown right away. I've kept it in the fridge for several days to test and it stayed green the whole time. The lemon keeps it from browning.

You have to keep it in an air-tight container though. So it doesn't oxidize.

Keto Green Smoothie in a glass and keto smoothie in a small pitcher one next to the other and lemon wedges around both

HOW TO MAKE A LOW CARB SMOOTHIE KETO

The best way to make a low carb smoothie keto is to avoid adding any fruit other than lemon and avocado. Avocado is a fruit but it's very low in sugar and high in fat which is what we want here, right?

It has only 3g of sugar which come mostly from the lemon actually. Net carbs are only about 7g and fat is at 11g. Perfect breakfast! It kept me full all morning.

It does take some getting used to but after the third sip all three, my husband, my daughter and me started really liking it. It's the weirdest thing. You give it a sip and think: meh. then you give it another sip and think: oh, it's not that bad actually. Then you give it another sip, and think: wait a second, I think I actually like it.

The funny thing is, this happened to all three of us! Isn't that crazy? I actually thought my daughter wouldn't like it but she drank a whole serving of it.

- Prep Time: 5 Minutes
- Total Time: 5 Minutes
- Servings: 2 People

A low-carb high fat Keto Smoothie to snack on or to have for breakfast! No sugary fruit, no sweeteners, only low carb veggies, high fat avocado and ginger, lemon and cilantro for that special flavor!

Ingredients

- 1 cup cold water
- 1 cup baby spinach
- 1/2 cup cilantro
- 1 inch ginger peeled
- 3/4 English cucumber peeled
- 1/2-1 lemon peeled
- 1 cup frozen avocado

Instructions

Add all ingredients to a high speed blender and blend until smooth.

Store in an air-tight container such as a mason jar in the fridge for up to 3 days.

Nutrition

Calories: 148kcal | Carbohydrates: 13g | Protein: 2g | Fat: 11g | Saturated Fat: 1g | Sodium: 28mg | Potassium: 653mg | Fiber: 6g | Sugar: 2g | Vitamin A: 1905IU | Vitamin C: 26.2mg | Calcium: 49mg | Iron: 1.3mg

15

PAN-FRIED ASPARAGUS TIPS WITH LEMON JUICE AND LEMON ZEST

Pan-Fried Asparagus Tips with
Lemon Juice and Lemon Zest

This simple and amazingly delicious recipe for Pan-Fried
Asparagus Tips with Lemon Juice and Lemon Zest has only three

ingredients and it's a perfect side dish to make for guests! Use Side Dishes to find more recipes like this one.

PIN Pan-Fried Asparagus Tips to make it later!

Pan-Fried Asparagus Tips with Lemon Juice and Lemon Zest found on KalynsKitchen.com

Every spring I look forward to the arrival of low-priced asparagus in the grocery store. Take a peek at my Asparagus Recipes and you can tell I love asparagus! I'm also a fan of the "less is more" approach when it comes to cooking it as a side dish. I've tried so many good asparagus recipes, but the asparagus side dish I make most often for guests is this Pan-Fried Asparagus Tips with Lemon Juice and Lemon Zest with only three ingredients: asparagus, olive oil, and a lemon.

If I make this recipe when I'm having guests, I like to use just the asparagus tips and save the thicker parts of the asparagus stalk to cook using a different method. If that doesn't work for you, cook the thicker parts of the asparagus stalks for a couple of minutes before you add the tips. Recently I had some gorgeous asparagus and decided to give this recipe photo update. And this delicious recipe for Pan-Fried Asparagus Tips was first posted back in 2012, so I'm guessing it will be new to many of you; hope you enjoy trying it!

Pan-Fried Asparagus Tips with Lemon Juice and Lemon Zest process shots collage

HOW TO MAKE PAN-FRIED ASPARAGUS TIPS WITH LEMON JUICE AND LEMON ZEST:

(Scroll down for complete printable recipe.)

· · ·

Before you start to cook the asparagus, use a lemon zester (affiliate link) or fine cheese greater to remove most of the lemon zest (grated bright yellow lemon skin.) When the zest is removed, cut the lemon in half and squeeze the juice.

Trim asparagus so you just have the tips, or if you're using the whole pieces trim the woody ends and cut asparagus pieces in half, keeping the thicker ends separate from the tips.

Then heat the olive oil in a large pan and lay asparagus in a single layer as much as you can. (Put the thicker ends in first if you're cooking the whole pieces, then add the tips after about about two minutes.)

Cook asparagus over medium-high heat about 4-5 minutes.

Then turn off heat, pour lemon juice over asparagus, plate it, and sprinkle with lemon zest.

Serve Pan-Fried Asparagus Tips with Lemon Juice and Lemon Zest hot and wait for raves from your guests!

Pan-Fried Asparagus Tips with Lemon Juice and Lemon Zest found on KalynsKitchen.com

OTHER TASTY RECIPES FOR ASPARAGUS

Low-Carb Sheet Pan Meals with Asparagus ~ Kalyn's Kitchen

Shaved Asparagus Salad ~ She Wears Many Hats

Roasted Asparagus and Mushrooms with "Everything" Bagel Seasoning ~ Kalyn's Kitchen

Spring Lettuce Salad with Roasted Asparagus ~ Recipe Girl

Low-Carb Chicken and Asparagus Bake with Creamy Cheesy Curry Sauce ~ Kalyn's Kitchen

Pickled Peppered Asparagus ~ A Farmgirl's Dabbles<

Pan-Fried Asparagus Tips with Lemon Juice and Lemon Zest
PRINT
PAN-FRIED ASPARAGUS TIPS WITH LEMON JUICE AND LEMON ZEST

yield 2 SERVINGS prep time 5 MINUTES cook time 5 MINUTES total time 10 MINUTES

Pan-Fried Asparagus Tips with Lemon Juice and Lemon Zest is one of my favorite ways to cook asparagus when I have dinner guests, and this easy but WOW asparagus recipe has only 3 ingredients!

INGREDIENTS

1/2 lb. asparagus tips (from one pound of asparagus, save the rest of the asparagus to cook another way)

1 T good *q*uality olive oil

1 lemon, remove all zest, then cut lemon in half and s*q*ueeze the juice.

INSTRUCTIONS

Cut 4-5 inch long tips from one pound of asparagus (saving the thicker stalk ends for another recipe, or see the note at the end if you're making 4 servings and want to use the whole pound of asparagus.)

Zest the lemon, then cut lemon in half and remove any noticeable seeds. Squeeze lemon juice into a small dish.

Heat the olive oil in the largest frying pan you have. I used my favorite non-stick Green Pan (affiliate link), but any good frying pan will work.

Add asparagus in a single layer and turn heat to medium-high. Cook asparagus 4-5 minutes, turning about once a minute. Asparagus is done when the thickest part of the stalk can be pierced fairly easily with a fork but asparagus still has some snap to it, and asparagus is starting to brown.

Turn off heat, then pour over desired amount of lemon juice. (Use all the juice if you're a lemon fan like I am.)

Arrange asparagus on a plate, sprinkle with lemon zest and serve immediately.

If you want to cook the whole pound of asparagus, trim the woody ends, then cut asparagus into two pieces, keeping the ends and the tips separate. Cook the ends about 2 minutes before you add the tips to the pan, then add the tips and cook 4-5 minutes more as above.

NOTES

This recipe was inspired by a recipe for cooking asparagus in Fine Cooking Magazine.

Nutrition information:

Amount Per Serving: CALORIES: 173TOTAL FAT: 7gSATURATED FAT: 1gUNSATURATED FAT: 6gCHOLESTEROL: 0mgSODIUM: 90mgCARBOHYDRATES: 5.2gFIBER: 5gSUGAR: 18gPROTEIN: 4g

16

ALMOND COOKIES DIPPED IN DARK CHOCOLATE (VEGAN – SUGAR FREE)

These Almond Cookies Dipped In Dark Chocolate (Vegan – Sugar Free) are my go to for when I want cookies and chocolate at the same time. (trust me, it happens) I couldn't of made this happen without Lakanto's Dark Chocolate Bar sweetened with monkfruit making these babies (in their entirety) not only vegan but gluten free and sugar flipping free!

Refined sugar is super addicting and wreaks havoc on the body in so many ways. I'm so happy to now have this sugar alternative so I can make all the treats, snacks, and bakes I want without sacrificing texture, flavor, sweetness, and most importantly, MY HEALTH! Lakanto's Monkfruit is an eQual substitution too so there won't be any crazy measurements. I'm going to give you the lowdown on this sweetener and why I only use mostly this now. Although I do love maple syrup and coconut nectar, this by far takes the cake for me when sweetening things up in the kitchen.

ABOUT LAKANTO MONKFRUIT SWEETENER

ONLY all natural, zero calorie, zero glycemic sweetener. Lakanto Sweetners are sugar free and have none of the bitter chemical after taste like Stevia and Xylitol.

PROPRIETARY mixture of the highest purity Monk Fruit extract & Non-GMO erythritol. Lakanto is a perfect sweetener for blood sugar and weight management.

1:1 SUGAR REPLACEMENT – Unlike monk fruit in the raw that has a light yeast flake feel; Lakanto has a perfect mix of monk fruit and erythritol (naturally found in many fruits and vegetables) to match the sweetness of sugar and maintain 1 for 1 sugar replacement.

ZERO EFFECT on blood sugar or insulin levels, making it a great sweetener for blood sugar and weight management. Ideal for sports enthusiasts, ketosis diets and those trying to watch their sugar consumption.

CLASSIC & GOLDEN | Golden Lakanto is a brown sugar substitute and the Classic White is a white sugar substitute. They use Non GMO Eurythritol and they don't use Xylitol that can cause gas.

DESCRIPTION

Lakanto Monk Fruit Sweetener is the only zero calorie, zero glycemic sweetener that is just like sugar without the bad side effects. It is made from Monk Fruit which was used for centuries in eastern traditional herbalism to increase chi and well-being, earning it the nickname "The Immortals' Fruit". They still grow and harvest Monk Fruit for LAKANTO® in the same pristine area and according to traditional and environmental methods.

YIELD: 12-14 COOKIES

PREP TIME: 5 MINUTES COOK TIME: 15 MINUTES TOTAL TIME: 20 MINUTES

Where chewy cookies meet dark chocolate for an awesomely sweet sugar free snack you can feel good about! Recipe video above!

Ingredients:

- 2 cups almond meal
- 1/2 tsp baking soda
- pinch of salt
- pinch of cinnamon
- 1/4 cup Lakanto Monkfruit Sweetener
- 4 tsp coconut oil, melted
- 4 tbsp almond milk
- 1 flax egg
- 1 tsp vanilla extract
- 1/2 tsp almond extract

Topping

- 1 - 3oz Lakanto Dark Chocolate Bar, melted
- handful of shredded coconut
- handful of sliced almonds

Directions:

Preheat oven to 350F and line baking sheet with parchment paper.

In a large bowl combine all ingredients except for the toppings. Mix well.

Take double tbsp size portions, roll into a ball and place on baking sheet. Alternatively you can use a cookie scoop of 1tbsp portions (cookies will be slightly smaller).

When all cookies are on baking sheet, slightly flatten with the palm of your hand.

Bake for 15 minutes or until slightly golden on edges.

Remove from oven and let cool completely before dipping them in chocolate.

While the cookies are cooling melt down dark chocolate using the double boiler method of in the oven. I don't use a microwave so I can't tell you how many minutes for that.

Once the chocolate is melted and cookies are cooled line a cookie rack or cutting board with parchment paper and make room in your freezer. Dip one side of the cookies in the melted chocolate, sprinkle with either coconut shreds or almond slices, then place in the freezer to set for 5-10 minutes.

Remove cookies from freezer and enjoy right away with some almond milk or store in an air tight container. Will last up to a week. Enjoy!

Nutritional Information

- Calories per serving 90
- Calories from fat 45
- Total Fat 5g8%
- Saturated Fat 2g9%
- Cholesterol 0mg0%
- Sodium 20mg1%
- Carbohydrates 10g3%
- Dietary Fiber .5g4%
- Vitamin A0%
- Vitamin C0%
- Calcium0%
- Iron0%
- Sugars 6g
- Protein 1g

17

CAULIFLOWER LOW CARB PALEO VEGAN STUFFING

This Cauliflower Low Carb Paleo Vegan Stuffing is made entirely from vegetables but has all the flavor of traditional stuffing! Whole30, gluten free and SO delicious!

Low Carb Cauliflower Stuffing - Made entirely from vegetables but has all the flavor of traditional bread stuffing! It's super easy, whole30 compliant, paleo, vegan, gluten free and SO delicious! Perfect for Thanksgiving or Christmas!

This Keto Low Carb Riced Cauliflower Stuffing is a real thing that exists in this universe and it RLY RLY needs to be happening on a Thanksgiving table near you in your VERY immediately real-person life.

A table so near that it is IN YOUR KITCHEN RIGHT NOW. Or it's in the kitchen of wherever you are spending this glorious day of ALL THINGS DELICIOUS FOOD.

Every good memory of my family Thanksgivings revolve around my Grandma's SUPER easy gluten free stuffing, scalloped sweet potatoes, and her paleo sweet potato casserole in the slow cooker.

Are you seeing the trend? ALL THE CARBS.

As I age (says the 26-almost-27-year-old) I have been TRYING to reduce my carb intake a little bit. Real

Which is where the idea of this cauliflower low carb paleo vegan stuffing came from. We've talked about it eleventy billion times: cauliflower is our miracle veggie friend that can do all kinds of crazy and wondrous things that make us think we are eating unhealthy foods (mango chicken with coconut cauliflower rice, I'm looking at you!) but – PSYCH – VEGGIES YO.

Adding "can make you feel like you're face-planting into cozy, herby stuffing-with-NO-bread" to the "special skills" section of cauli's resume RN.

Have to give a shot-out to Grandma for this recipe, 'cause I PRETTY much took HER recipe – the spices/veggies/generally delicious things that she uses – and just chucked in a little vegetable action instead of bread. And then I also chucked the veggie version inside of vegan stuffed butternut s**q**uash and it was magic.

You know when you do something and just PRAY PRAY PRAY that it works? That is my life almost always with recipes, and most DEFINITELY in this low carb stuffing recipe situation.

I mean, cauli can do A LOT. But mimic pillowy-soft-perfectly-crispy bread? MMMMMMMMM. UNSURE.

Internet besties. THIS IS THE REAL DEAL. The BEST vegan stuffing. Liiiike, it W-O-R-K-E-D. SOSOSO WELL.

Crunchy carrots, zesty onions and crunchy celery mish-mash together with tender-crisp cauliflower and simmer in a pool of salty broth and herb-a-LICIOUS, earthy spices to create EVERY. SINGLE. Flavor profile that your mouth expects when you promise to fill it with STUFFING.

Cauliflower low carb paleo vegan stuffing is the kind of healthy little side dish that you almost don't want to like, because it feels like SUCH a crime when Grandma has been slaving over her carb-inclusive recipe all day long. But, then you taste it, and SO LONG BREAD. THERES A NEW SIDE DISH IN TOWN.

And its name is vegetables forever and ever the end. Not even mad about it one bit. <–Pro tip, put some low carb sugar free keto cranberry sauce on top. You're welcome.

Make room for a little from-the-ground-goodness this Thanksgiving.

- Prep time: 10 m
- Cook time: 30 m
- Servings: 4

Ingredients

- 1 1/2 tablespoons Olive Oil
- 1 cup Diced Onion, about half a large onion
- 1 cup Chopped Celery
- 1 1/2 tablespoons Minced Garlic
- 6 cups Cauliflower, cut into small, bite-sized florets, 560g
- 2 tablespoons Fresh Chopped Parsley, minced, plus additional for garnish
- 1 teaspoon Poultry Seasoning
- 1/2 teaspoon Ground Sage

- 1/2 teaspoon Sea Salt, plus more to taste
- Black Pepper
- 1/2 cup Low Sodium Chicken Broth, or vegetable broth

Directions

Heat the olive oil in a large frying pan on medium-high heat. Add in the onion, celery and garlic and cook, stirring frequently, until the onion is golden brown and tender, about 8 minutes.

Reduce the heat to medium and stir in the cauliflower. Cook until the cauliflower just begins to soften and brown, stirring frequently, or about 10 minutes.

Add in the parsley, poultry seasoning, sage, salt* and a pinch of pepper and cook one minute.

Stir in the broth, cover, and cook until the cauliflower is tender and the liquid is absorbed, about 10 minutes.

Season with salt if needed, garnish with additional parsley and DEVOUR!

Notes

If you're salt-sensitive, you may want 1/2 tsp.

Nutrition facts

- Calories 101.9
- Total fat 5.5g
- Saturated fat 0.7g
- Polyunsaturated fat
- Monounsaturated fat
- Cholestorel 0.0mg
- Sodium 429.2mg
- Potassium 573.2mg
- Total carbohydrate
- Dietary fiber 4.7g
- Sugars 4.9g
- Protein 3.8g

18

MUSHROOM AND CAULIFLOWER VEGAN SHEPHERDS PIE {LOW CARB}

The British classic gets a vegetarian makeover with mushrooms and cauliflower. The result is a delicious low carb vegetarian shepherd's pie recipe that the whole family will love!

Vegan Shepherds Pie Recipe - the British classic gets a vegan makeover and lightened up with mushrooms and cauliflower. Try this low carb, vegan and gluten free Vegan Shepherds Pie today!

Shepherd's pie was a classic that many households in Australia and Britain grew up with and started as a way for people to make left-over scraps of meat and vegetables into a delicious meal.

Not only are they amazingly versatile, they are also good for you as well.

Here are some interesting facts on how mushrooms are beneficial for a healthy heart:

- Mushrooms contain a type of fibre that naturally helps to lower blood cholesterol
- Mushrooms are low in fat, sodium and kilojoules, helping to control weight and blood pressure.
- Mushrooms, along with vegetables, help to reduce the risk of heart disease.
- Research shows that eating mushrooms can help to lower the bad cholesterol in the blood, which can help prevent narrowing of the arteries.

While the health benefits of mushrooms are a plus, they are always a staple in our house because of their delicious versatility.

It's funny to think that my once mushroom hating husband now regularly requests mushroom meals such as my mushroom quinoa burgers, vegan mushroom alfredo and mushroom soup.

Continuing the makeover of my vegan shepherd's pie I've used cauliflower in place of potato, which works hand in hand with mushrooms healthy heart benefits, thanks to the sulforaphane in cauliflower.

Sulforaphane has been found to significantly improve blood pressure and kidney function. It also makes this a wonderful low-carb dish that is also significantly less stodgy than the original.

Vegan Shepherds Pie Recipe - the British classic gets a vegan makeover and lightened up with mushrooms and cauliflower. Try this low carb, vegan and gluten free Vegan Shepherds Pie today | DeliciousEveryday.com

Be sure to check out the Power of Mushrooms website from the Australian Mushroom Growers Association for more amazing recipes and ideas for using fresh mushrooms!

The British classic gets a vegetarian makeover with mushrooms and cauliflower. The result is a delicious low carb vegetarian shepherd's pie recipe that the whole family will love!

- Prep Time: 30 minutes
- Cook Time: 30 minutes
- Total Time: 1 hour
- Servings: 4 people

Ingredients

- 650 g cauliflower (1 1/2 pounds)
- 2 tbs olive oil
- 1 onion diced
- 2 medium sized carrots peeled and diced
- 1 celery stalk diced
- 3 cloves garlic chopped
- 10 g dried wild mushrooms reconstituted in 2 1/2 tbs boiling water (1/3 oz)
- 500 g mushrooms diced (1 pound)
- 1 tbs thyme leaves roughly chopped
- 1 tbs tomato paste
- 1/4 cup red wine
- 1 cup vegetable stock
- salt and pepper to taste
- 2 tbs olive oil
- 3 tbsp nutritional yeast
- 1 tbs dijon mustard
- 1 tsp salt
- 2 tsp thyme leaves

- 1 pinch ground nutmeg
- US Customary - Metric

Instructions

Preheat the oven to 200 celsius (400 fahrenheit).

Chop the cauliflower into roughly equal sized pieces and add to a large saucepan. Cover with water and bring to a boil. Season with salt and cook the cauliflower until tender. Drain.

Place a large frying pan over a medium heat. Add the olive oil, onion, carrots and celery. Cook until slightly golden and caramelised. Add the mushrooms in 6 parts, making sure each batch is cooked before adding the next.

Remove the wild mushrooms from the boiling water, reserving the water, and roughly chop. Add to the mushrooms along with the tomato paste. Increase the heat to medium-high and add the red wine. Cook until the red wine has almost evaporated before adding the mushroom soaking liquid and vegetable stock. Reduce the heat to low and simmer for 5 to 10 minutes or until roughly half of the liquid has been absorbed. Remove from the heat.

Place the cauliflower in a food processor or high powered blender along with 2 tbs olive oil, the nutritional yeast, mustard, salt and thyme leaves. Blend until smooth and taste. Adjust seasonings as required and add the nutmeg and blend for a further minute.

Divide the mushrooms between 4 large ramekins and top with the cauliflower mash. Bake for 20 minutes or until lightly golden.

Notes

Nutritional Yeast (sometimes called savoury yeast flakes) is available in health food stores. Make sure you purchase nutritional yeast and NOT brewers yeast as they are very different things. You can also purchase nutritional yeast online from amazon (see link in recipe) as well as in Australia from here.

Nutrition

Serving: 400g | Calories: 265kcal | Carbohydrates: 23g | Protein: 11g | Fat: 15g | Saturated Fat: 2g | Sodium: 970mg | Potassium: 1212mg | Fiber: 7g | Sugar: 9g | Vitamin A: 5385IU | Vitamin C: 89.8mg | Calcium: 67mg | Iron: 2.4mg

19

CLASSIC EGG SALAD

This classic egg salad recipe is the perfect make ahead dish. Great for breakfast on toast, for lunch in a wrap, or over salad or in a sandwich. Sometimes I just eat it with a spoon right out of the container!

This classic egg salad recipe can be enjoyed for breakfast on

toast, or for lunch in a wrap, over salad or in a sandwich. Sometimes I just eat it with a spoon right out of the container!

This classic egg salad recipe can be enjoyed for breakfast on
toast, or for lunch in a wrap, over salad or in a sandwich. Sometimes I just eat it with a spoon right out of the container!

This is gluten-free, low-carb, keto friendly and Whole30 if you
use compliant mayonnaise such homemade or this mayo by
Primal Kitchen (affiliate link).

This will last in the refrigerator 4 to 5 days.

WHAT DO YOU PUT IN YOUR EGG SALAD?

I keep my egg salad pretty simple, a little mayonnaise, red
onion, salt, pepper, paprika and some chives, for garnish. This is
the way I like to make my egg salad but you can totally make this
your own! Here's some suggestions:

- Add pickle juice or diced pickles
- Include some veggies like chopped celery or carrots for
  texture
- Add some Dijon mustard
- Add some protein such as diced cooked shrimp, it's
  delish!
- Swap the chives for fresh dill
- Try adding a few capers

This classic egg salad recipe can be enjoyed for breakfast on
toast, or for lunch in a wrap, over salad or in a sandwich. Sometimes I just eat it with a spoon right out of the container!

- PREP TIME: 5 Mins
- COOK TIME: 20 Mins
- TOTAL TIME: 25 Mins
- YIELD:4 SERVINGS

This classic egg salad recipe can be enjoyed for breakfast on
toast, or for lunch in a wrap, over salad or in a sandwich. Sometimes I just eat it with a spoon right out of the container!

Ingredients

- 6 hard boiled eggs, peeled and chopped
- 3 tablespoons mayonnaise
- 1 teaspoon finely chopped red onion
- 1/4 teaspoon kosher salt
- fresh black pepper, to taste
- 1/8 teaspoon sweet paprika, for garnish
- chopped chives, for garnish

Instructions

Combine all the ingredients and refrigerate until ready to eat.

Nutritional facts

Serving: 1/2 cup, Calories: 185kcal, Carbohydrates: 1g, Protein: 9.5g, Fat: 15.5g, Saturated Fat: 3.5g, Cholesterol: 282mg, Sodium: 215.5mg, Sugar: 2g

20

VEGETARIAN LOADED ZUCCHINI SKINS

One of my all-time favorite appetizers has always been loaded potato skins. I still get cravings for that combination of cheese, sour cream and bacon. If you want to adhere to the vegetarian lifestyle while remaining keto, the solution is all in the seasoning!

I love using chopped mushrooms in place of bacon bits. As you know, we eat with our eyes so appearance is everything. When seasoned and cooked properly mushrooms can fool, or at least entice, most of my carnivorous friends. Smoked paprika is a great tool in vegetarian cooking because it adds depth with a beautiful smoky aroma and flavor. These seasoned little bits of mushroom melt into the layers of shredded cheddar and pepper jack just like bacon would! Add a little salt, sour cream, and chives to garnish and your meat eating friends won't be complaining!

As for the skins, I opted to use a variety of squash called "Mexican Squash" because it is stout, round, and looks more like the traditional potato skin shape. One entire squash is about the size of a large potato and it holds up to the baking process without getting limp or mushy! These are readily available in most grocery stores but if you can't find Mexican squash, typical zucchini will work, too.

These loaded zucchini skins are great as appetizers or as part of a simple keto dinner. I found that they even reheat well the next day!

Ingredients

- 3 large Mexican squash, halved and seeds removed*
- 1 teaspoon salt
- 3 whole cremini mushrooms, diced*
- 1 teaspoon olive oil
- 2 teaspoons Smoked Paprika
- 1 tablespoon Worcestershire sauce**
- ½ teaspoon salt
- 2 ounces shredded pepper jack cheese
- 2 ounces shredded cheddar cheese
- 3 tablespoons sour cream
- 2 tablespoons chopped chives

Instruction

- Heat oven to 375°F. Prepare the squash by washing well, removing the ends and slicing into halves.
- Using a spoon, carefully scrape the seeds from each zucchini halve and discard.
- Sprinkle the zucchini skins with salt and let sit to draw out some of the water. Pat dry.
- Drizzle the diced mushrooms with oil, smoked paprika, ½ tsp salt, and Worcestershire and toss to coat.

- Arrange the zucchini and mushrooms on a baking sheet and roast for 8-10 minutes or until the mushrooms begin to brown and sizzle.
- Remove the zucchini from the oven and top with the roasted mushrooms and shredded pepper jack and cheddar cheese.
- Bake for 5-10 minutes or until the cheese is melted and bubbling.
- Top with sour cream and chives.

Nutrition facts

This makes a total of 6 servings of Vegetarian Loaded Zucchini Skins. Each serving comes out to be 108.5 Calories, 8.25g Fat, 2.82g Net Carbs, and 5.76g Protein.

21

VEGETARIAN KETO "CRAB" CAKES

Crab cakes can easily be made keto with a simple swap for bread crumbs, but today we are going even further to make a keto crab cake that is crab-less! That's right, a vegetarian-friendly crab cake with absolutely zero meat that still achieves that flakey interior and a crisp buttery crust!

The secret ingredient in these crabless cakes is hearts of palm. This vegetable is harvested from the core of many different varieties of palm trees and is nutrient dense yet low in net carbs. Its flavor could be compared to an artichoke in that it's mild and slightly briny but pairs well with cheesy dips or a buttery crumb coating. The texture of this vegetable is very similar to lump crab meat when carefully broken apart with a fork or gently with clean hands.

Because there is some moisture in the hearts of palm, this recipe calls for almond flour in the crab mixture as well as a bit more to coat the cakes. This keeps them from falling apart while giving you a beautifully browned and crisp coating. Pan frying is also crucial to keeping them together and gives the cakes the proper texture.

Serve these crabless cakes with your favorite dipping sauce or as a patty on a bed of lettuce! These cakes are best served immediately but will hold up to reheating for up to three days. These crabless cakes make a great option for lunch or even a keto dinner.

Ingredients

- 1 can hearts of palm, drained
- 2 tablespoons mayonnaise
- 1 teaspoon Old Bay seasoning
- 1 tablespoon parsley
- 1/4 cup almond flour
- 1 large egg, beaten
- 1 tablespoon (10g) onion, diced
- 1 teaspoon butter
- 3 tablespoons almond meal
- 2 tablespoons Parmesan cheese
- 4 tablespoons avocado oil

Direction

Drain the hearts of palm. Using a fork, shred the pieces until they resemble crab meat.

Mix in the Old Bay, mayonnaise, almond flour, beaten egg, and parsley to combine.

In a skillet heat the butter over medium heat and sauté the diced onion until translucent then gently fold into the hearts of palm mixture.

Place the almond meal and Parmesan cheese in a shallow

dish. Mix together. Separate the mixture into six equal balls roll. Press into the mixture so that each ball is flattened into a patting and covered with the coating.

Place each patty on a baking sheet, top with any remaining coating.

Preheat a skillet over medium-high heat. Add the avocado oil. Fry each patty, two at a time, turning carefully to brown each side. Serve hot.

Nutritional facts

This makes a total of 3 servings, two cakes per serving of Vegetarian Keto Crab Cakes. Each serving comes out to be 434.24 Calories, 41.01g Fat, 5.47g Net Carbs, and 10.03g Protein.

22

VEGETARIAN KETO CLUB SALAD

Being keto doesn't have to be hard for all you vegetarians out there! Whether you have been doing keto for a while now, or have just made the switch, it can seem like every recipe you come across is meat heavy and low on the veggies. If you have been used to eating a diet that was primarily fruits and vegetables it can certainly leave you feeling like you are missing out and maybe even craving some of that fresh and crunchy texture. My solution? The simple but oh so filling keto salad!

Yes, it's different from a traditional club sandwich or even a club salad, but the flavors will have you happily munching on vegetables without missing the bread or the meat! The makings of a satisfying salad come with a few integral parts: the crunch factor, the creamy and savory dressing, and the kick. This salad is loaded with crisp romaine lettuce and cucumber and balanced with cheddar cheese cubes, hardboiled egg and a creamy mayonnaise based dressing. Then, the spicy kick of Dijon mustard brings this salad together in an explosion of flavor.

Surprised I could get so excited about a simple salad? So was I! You could certainly add meat to this dish but the balance of flavors is great without! The calorie count is high on this salad because of the rich dressing and cheese. It's high in fat and moderate on protein so it's perfect for a keto lunch or dinner!

Missing croutons? Give our recent crouton recipe a try.

Ingredients

- 2 tablespoons sour cream
- 2 tablespoons mayonnaise
- ½ teaspoon garlic powder
- ½ teaspoon onion powder
- 1 teaspoon dried parsley
- 1 tablespoon milk
- 3 large hard boiled eggs, sliced
- 4 ounces cheddar cheese, cubed
- 3 cups romaine lettuce, torn into pieces
- ½ cup cherry tomatoes, halved
- 1 cup diced cucumber
- 1 tablespoon dijon mustard

Instruction

Prepare the dressing by mixing the sour cream, mayonnaise, and dried herbs until combined.

Add one tablespoon of milk and mix. If the dressing seems too thick, add another tablespoon of milk. Don't forget to add another tablespoon of milk to the final fat/protein/carb count if you do!

Layer your salad with the fresh veggies, cheese, and sliced egg. Add a spoonful of Dijon mustard in the center.

Drizzle with the prepared dressing, about 2 tablespoons for one serving, then toss to coat.

Nutritional facts

This makes a total of 3 single-servings of Vegetarian Keto Cobb Salad with 2 tablespoons of dressing per serving. Each serving comes out to be 329.67 Calories, 26.32 g Fat, 4.83 g Net Carbs, and 16.82 g Protein.

23

CRUSTLESS BROCCOLI CHEDDAR QUICHE

Broccoli and cheese is one of my favorite *q*uiche combinations! This low-carb Crustless Broccoli Cheddar Quiche is light and delicious, perfect for breakfast or brunch (or even a light dinner)!

Spinach and Ricotta Quiche and Chicken Quiche are so popular on my site, but I often get asked how to make it crustless. For this low-carb version, I made this with no crust, and added lots of broccoli plus I used some light cream to give the eggs more of a creamier custard texture, as most quiches have rather than a spongier baked egg texture. This turned out delicious! I also love this perfect for sharing, bite-sized, crustless veggie and turkey quiche.

This quiche is low-carb, keto, gluten-free and easy! Add a salad on the side and it's the perfect vegetarian lunch.

BROCCOLI QUICHE VARIATIONS:

You can add some diced ham or bacon and use slightly less broccoli.

Try this with mozzarella cheese or Colby Jack cheese in place of cheddar.

You can swap more milk in place of the half & half cream, but the texture won't be as creamy, it will have a spongier texture.

Make them in individual ramekins in place of one large pie dish.

If you wish to use a crust, follow the directions for this recipe using a deeper pie dish, and use less broccoli.

Refriegerate 3 to 4 days. Reheat in the microwave or oven.

Broccoli and cheese is one of my favorite quiche combinations! This low-carb Crustless Broccoli Cheddar Quiche is light and delicious, perfect for breakfast or brunch (or even a light dinner)!

- Prep Time: 10 Mins
- Cook Time: 40 Mins
- Total Time: 50 Mins
- Yield:6 Servings

Broccoli and cheese is one of my favorite quiche combinations! This low-carb Crustless Broccoli Cheddar Quiche is light and delicious, perfect for breakfast or brunch (or even a light dinner)!

Ingredients

- cooking spray

- 3 cups chopped broccoli florets
- 1 cup grated cheddar cheese
- 2/3 cup 2% milk
- 1/4 cup half & half cream
- 5 large eggs
- 3/4 teaspoon kosher salt
- 1/8 teaspoon ground black pepper
- pinch freshly grated nutmeg

Instructions

Preheat your oven to 350 degrees. Spray a pie dish with oil.

Steam the chopped broccoli florets in the microwave with 1 tablespoon water until tender crisp and green but not mushy, about 2 1/2 to 3 minutes.

Evenly spread the broccoli in the dish and top it evenly with the grated cheddar cheese.

Make the custard mixture by whisking together the milk, half and half, eggs, salt, black pepper, and the nutmeg. Pour the custard into the dish and bake 35 to 40 minutes, until the center is set.

Cut the quiche into 6 pieces and serve.

Nutritional facts

Serving: 1slice, Calories: 174kcal, Carbohydrates: 5g, Protein: 12.5g, Fat: 12g, Saturated Fat: 6g, Cholesterol: 178mg, Sodium: 358mg, Fiber: 1.5g, Sugar: 3g

24

5-INGREDIENT GRAIN FREE GRANOLA (NO SUGAR)

This grain free granola is made without sugar! It's loaded with coconut, a variety of nuts, coconut oil and cinnamon. Paleo, gluten-free, low carb and low sugar.

The simpler the better these days! This granola is made with only five ingredients and comes together in a flash. Even though it's sugar free, it is crazy delicious!

Only 5 Ingredients

- unsweetened coconut flakes
- raw nuts: I used a blend of cashews, almonds, walnuts and pumpkin seeds
- chia seeds
- cinnamon
- coconut oil or butter, melted

All the ingredients for grain-free granola in a bowl.

How to Make Grain Free Granola

It truly doesn't get much easier than this... mix all of the ingredients together in a bowl and spread on a baking sheet lined with parchment paper. Make sure the mixture is spread evenly on the baking sheet. Bake until golden brown and enjoy! After completely cooled you can store in an airtight container. I like to store in the refrigerator or freezer so it stays extra crunchy.

Making grain free granola. All the granola in a bowl after stirring.

No Added Sugar

This recipe is inspired by Sarah Wilson's sugar-free granola recipe from I Quit Sugar. She suggests using rice malt syrup, but I made mine without the syrup and it turned out to be delicious. I can totally see why it's such a popular recipe. It does a great job of satisfying my craving for sweet and crunchy granola but without the grains and added sugar. It's so packed with healthy fats from the coconut, nuts and chia seeds so it's really quite filling. I love it on greek yogurt!

- Prep Time: 5 minutes
- Cook Time: 20 minutes
- Total Time: 25 minutes

- Yield: 15

Grain free granola made with a blend of coconut, a variety of nuts, coconut oil and cinnamon. It's crunchy, delicious and low in sugar.

Ingredients

- 3 cups unsweetened coconut flakes
- 2 cups raw nuts, roughly chopped (I used 1 cup raw cashews, 1/2 cup raw almonds, roughly chopped, 1/4 cup raw walnuts, 1/4 cup raw pumpkin seeds)
- 2 tablespoons chia seeds
- 1 teaspoon ground cinnamon
- 5 tablespoons coconut oil or butter, melted

Instructions

Preheat oven to 250°F and line a baking sheet with parchment paper.

Combine all ingredients in a bowl, mix thoroughly, and spread evenly on the sheet.

Bake 30-40 minutes until golden, rotating halfway through cooking time.

Remove from oven and allow to cool, then eat while it's still crispy.

NOTES

I like storing the granola in my fridge or freezer so it stays extra crunchy.

Nutrition

- Serving Size: 1/4 cup
- Calories: 169
- Sugar: 1g
- Fat: 16g
- Carbohydrates: 5g
- Fiber: 2g
- Protein: 4g

25

KETO LOW CARB ROASTED TOMATO SOUP RECIPE WITH FRESH TOMATOES

This easy low carb tomato soup recipe is bursting with roasted tomatoes & fresh basil. Who knew keto roasted tomato soup could be so delicious? There's a paleo option, too.

Keto Low Carb Roasted Tomato Soup Recipe - This easy low carb tomato soup recipe is bursting with roasted tomatoes & fresh basil. Who knew keto roasted tomato soup could be so delicious? There's a paleo option, too.

HOW TO MAKE ROASTED TOMATO SOUP LOW CARB & KETO

My love for roasted tomato basil soup goes back almost a decade. It all started at this cute little local Italian restaurant we have in the Twin Cities. My husband and I have been getting roasted tomato soup there for years, since we first started dating.

The soup is rich and incredibly thick. Although I have no idea exactly what they put into their roasted tomato soup recipe, I'm certain from the flavor that it definitely involves roasted tomatoes.

My roasted low carb tomato soup version is almost like that – warming, a little creamy, and bursting with the flavors of roasted tomatoes and fresh basil.

There's just one problem: most of the super thick tomato soup recipes are relatively high in carbs. That might seem surprising, but the natural sugar in tomatoes can add up if they are concentrated.

And, some roasted tomato soup recipes even use flour as a thickener. No, thanks!

So, how to make roasted tomato soup low carb? It's actually pretty simple. You thin it out with something delicious, like a good broth or some cream – or in the case of this keto tomato soup recipe, use both!

5-Ingredient Roasted Tomato Soup (Low Carb, Gluten-Free) - This easy 5-ingredient soup is bursting with roasted tomatoes and fresh basil. Low carb, gluten-free, grain-free, and keto, with a paleo option.

If carbs are not a factor, you can definitely increase the amount of tomatoes and decrease the broth, which will make a much thicker soup. Otherwise, check my tips in my low carb butternut squash soup recipe for ideas on how to thicken a soup without adding carbs.

Keto Low Carb Roasted Tomato Soup Recipe - This easy low carb tomato soup recipe is bursting with roasted tomatoes & fresh basil. Who knew keto roasted tomato soup could be so delicious? There's a paleo option, too.

OPTIONS & SHORTCUTS FOR KETO TOMATO SOUP

This low carb tomato soup recipe is pretty basic. There aren't too many ingredients, but the ones it does have are bursting with flavor. Truly.

That being said, there are a few steps involved – roasting the tomatoes, pureeing them, mixing them with the broth and herbs to make the soup, and finally adding the cream and basil. None of these are difficult, but sometimes you might want to save time.

HOW TO MAKE PALEO TOMATO SOUP

What about if you are paleo or dairy-free? No problem.

This roasted tomato soup recipe is easy to make paleo and dairy-free. Simply replace the heavy cream with coconut cream instead!

OTHER LOW CARB SOUP IDEAS

For another variation of keto tomato soup, try Cream of Tomato Soup. If you like cheese, that one has it added for even more creaminess. So good!

Cabbage soup with ground beef is another favorite comforting soup in my house.

Finally, don't forget to check out all the other low carb soup recipes!

Easy Garlic Parmesan Keto Biscuits Recipe (Gluten-Free) - Buttery keto biscuits with garlic and parmesan are perfect for holiday meals, weeknight dinners, and snacks. This gluten-free biscuits recipe is super easy, too!

WHAT TO SERVE WITH ROASTED TOMATO SOUP

Roasted tomato soup goes perfectly with just about anything having Italian flavors.

One of my favorite pairings is biscuits – try garlic Parmesan keto biscuits or simple 4-ingredient almond flour biscuits. If you like your tomato soup with croutons, you can make them from 5-ingredient keto paleo bread or even 90-second bread in a pinch.

Finally, don't forget the main dish after you're done with your soup. Make some simple oven baked chicken thighs, chicken Parmesan, or browse the other low carb dinner recipes.

HOW TO STORE LOW CARB TOMATO SOUP

You can store leftover keto tomato soup in the fridge and reheat as needed. Heavy cream does not curdle as easily as milk, so should be fine reheating. To be on the safe side, stir as you reheat.

CAN YOU FREEZE ROASTED TOMATO SOUP?

Yes! If at all possible, it's best to freeze it without the cream and add that only after thawing and reheating before serving.

But if you have to freeze leftovers, it should still probably be okay. Just make sure to thaw the soup first, and reheat slowly while stirring.

Even though there are a couple of steps involved in making this low carb roasted tomato soup, they are extremely easy and pretty much hands off. That makes it perfectly convenient to make while you prepare the rest of your dinner. I cannot wait to warm up with it after my next autumn or winter walk outside!

TOOLS TO MAKE LOW CARB TOMATO SOUP:

- Baking Sheet – I use this baking sheet in my kitchen all the time. It's one of my favorite kitchen tools.
- Parchment Paper – Parchment paper is recommended in my recipes all the time. I prefer to use it to keep food from sticking to my pan and to make clean-up easier.
- Blender – This professional grade blender works perfectly for pureeing your roasted tomatoes.
- Large Pot – You need a large pot to finish off this low carb tomato soup. This cookware set has the perfect size.

This easy low carb tomato soup recipe is bursting with roasted tomatoes & fresh basil. Who knew keto roasted tomato soup could be so delicious? There's a paleo option, too.

- Prep Time 5 minutes
- Cook Time 40 minutes

- Total Time 45 minutes
- Servings: 6
- US Customary - Metric

Ingredients

- 10 medium Roma tomato (cut into 1" cubes)
- 2 tbsp Olive oil
- 4 cloves Garlic (minced)
- 2 cup Chicken bone broth (or any chicken broth)
- 1 tbsp Herbs de Provence
- 1/2 tsp Sea salt
- 1/4 tsp Black pepper
- 1/4 cup Heavy cream (or coconut cream for paleo)
- 2 tbsp Fresh basil (cut into ribbons)
- Wholesome Yum Keto Sweeteners

Instructions

Preheat the oven to 400 degrees F (204 degrees C). Line a baking sheet with foil and grease lightly.

Toss the tomato chunks with olive oil and minced garlic. Arrange in a single layer on the baking sheet. Roast in the oven for about 20-25 minutes, until the skin on the tomatoes puckers.

Transfer the tomato chunks into a blender (including garlic and liquid in the pan) and puree until smooth. (This works best with a high power blender. You can try batches with a regular blender. Alternatively, use an immersion blender right in the pot you'll be using.)

Pour the tomato puree into a pot over medium heat. Add broth. Season with Herbs de Provence, sea salt and black pepper to taste. Simmer for 10-15 minutes.

Stir in the cream and basil.

Nutrition Facts

- Calories95

- Fat8g
- Protein3g
- Total Carbs1g
- Net Carbs1g
- Fiber0g
- Sugar 0g

26

VEGAN EGGPLANT SHAKSHUKA W/ TOFU SCRAMBLE

If you haven't had shakshuka before, you are in for a treat! This dish is loaded with a plethora of vegetables in a thick tomato sauce, topped with a flavor-packed tofu scramble, and ready in less than 30 minutes!

This eggplant shakshuka is perfect for breakfast, lunch or even dinner, and is SO easy to make. We love the fact that this dish uses simple and readily available ingredients and can be modified as you desire! Don't have access to Anaheim peppers? Just add more bell peppers! No olives? opt for capers or simply just leave it out! Not a fan of parsley? Cilantro makes a great substitute and pairs well with the flavors of the dis–the list can go on and on. We have seen so many different takes on this recipe, so we encourage you to make it your own and have fun with it!

This dish is inspired by the many vegan shakshuka's I enjoyed on my trip with Vibe Israel this past March (pictured above). It was the first time I had tried or even heard of the dish, and I knew that I had to recreate it as soon as I returned home. The egg and vegetable form of this dish actually originates from Tunisia and is popular in the Middle East and North Africa. I am excited to share my spin on it with you today!

We love to serve our eggplant shakshuka alongside our homemade pita bread or fresh sourdough from our local farmers market. It really steps up the dish and makes it much more filling and satisfying. Plus there is nothing better than fresh warm bread, right?!

Prep Time: 10 minutes

Cook Time: 20 minutes

Total Time: 30 minutes

Yield: 6 servings

If you haven't had shakshuka before, you are in for a treat! This dish is loaded with a plethora of vegetables in a thick tomato sauce, topped with a flavor-packed tofu scramble, and ready in less than 30 minutes!

Ingredients

- 2 tablespoons extra virgin olive oil
- ½ cup yellow onion, finely diced
- 1/2 medium red bell pepper, diced small (about 1/3 cup)
- 1 anaheim pepper, seeds removed and diced small (about 1/2 cup)
- 4 cloves garlic, finely minced
- 1 small (6-inch) eggplant, diced small

- 1 teaspoon smoked paprika
- 1 teaspoon ground cumin
- Pinch of cayenne pepper
- Optional spices: 1/8 teaspoon each of cinnamon and ground coriander
- 1 (28 oz.) can fire roasted whole peeled tomatoes*
- 3 tablespoons tomato paste
- 1 teaspoon coconut sugar
- 1 bay leaf
- 1/4 cup chopped fresh parsley leaves + more to top
- 5 kalamata or green olives, pitted and sliced + more to top
- Salt and pepper, to taste
- 1/2 recipe of our Basic Tofu Scramble
- Pita bread, to serve

Instructions

Heat 1 tablespoon of olive oil in a large cast-iron skillet (or rimmed metal pan) over medium heat. Add the onion, bell pepper, Anaheim pepper, and garlic. Sauté for 3-4 minutes or until soft and fragrant. Add the spices and cook for 1 minute more.

Add the eggplant and sauté for an additional 3 minutes or so until it begins to soften, adding more oil if needed. Mix in the can of tomatoes, tomato paste, sugar, and bay leaf. Allow the tomatoes to cook down, stirring occasionally, for about 15 and 20 minutes or until it resembles a chunky sauce.* If you have not already prepared the tofu scramble, you can do it now to save time.

Remove the bay leaf and season with salt and pepper to taste.

Top with the tofu scramble along with a garnish of olives and parsley. Serve as is or with pita bread, pasta or your bread of choice.

Notes

If you don't have fire roasted, no worries! A 28 oz. can of regular tomatoes will work just fine.

If you would prefer a smoother texture, you can scoop 1/2-

3/4 of the sauce in the blender and blend until smooth and then add it back in.

Store leftovers covered in the refrigerator up to 4 days or in the freezer up to 1 month. Reheat on the stovetop until completely warmed through.

Nutrition Facts

- Calories 155
- Total Fat 7.8g 12%
- Cholesterol 0mg 0%
- Sodium 338mg 14%
- Total Carbohydrate 15.7g 5%
- Sugars 6.9g
- Protein 5.3g 11%
- Vitamin A9%
- Vitamin C78%
- Calcium7%
- Iron14%

27

VEGAN TERIYAKI GRILLED EGGPLANT

Satisfy your teriyaki cravings with this light and low-carb grilled eggplant! Perfect as a vegan side dish to pair with stir-fry cauli-rice or pan-seared tofu, this quick and simple veggie puts an Asian spin on one of my favorite veggies: the eggplant.

Teriyaki was always one of my go-to orders when eating at a sushi restaurant. Whether it was teriyaki fried tofu or just a plate of teriyaki vegetables, I always felt like I was making a healthier choice, until I realized just how much sugar went into the sauce I loved so much. I was so excited when I tried to duplicate the sauce using liquid aminos and swerve and the taste was just as I remembered.

Liquid aminos is a soy sauce alternative that is gluten-free and contains 16 of the 20 amino acids that make a complete protein. Though it won't add a significant amount of protein to your diet, it is a great addition for vegetarians and vegans as a flavor enhancer and boost of essential amino acids. It's a delicious companion in everything from salad dressings to marinades and soups!

This sauce is fairly thin and is more of a marinade than a traditional teriyaki sauce. Because the eggplant is repeatedly brushed in the sauce, it soaks in all the flavor while caramelizing on the outside. You can prepare this on an outdoor grill lined with foil or if you live in a place where grilling is impossible, a countertop electric grill works great.

Ingredients

- 1/4 cup sesame oil
- 1/2 cup liquid aminos
- 2 cloves garlic, peeled and pressed
- 1 tablespoon ground ginger
- 2 tablespoons granulated swerve
- 2 medium eggplants
- 1 tablespoon toasted sesame seeds

Direction

Combine sesame oil, liquid aminos, garlic, ginger, and swerve into a sauce pan and whisk together over medium heat.

Bring the sauce to a light simmer, stirring frequently until it begins to thicken slightly. Remove from heat.

Remove the stems from the eggplants and slice into 1/8 in slices. You will get approximately five full slices from each eggplant for a total of ten slices.

Brush each slice of eggplant with the teriyaki sauce and place on a hot grill.

Sear each side, brushing with more sauce as it caramelizes.

Garnish with toasted sesame seeds and serve with remaining sauce.

Nutrition

This makes a total of 5 servings of Vegan Teriyaki Grilled Eggplant. Each serving comes out to be 163.4 Calories, 12.07g Fat, 6.98g Net Carbs, and 3.72g Protein.

28

EGG AND GREENS BOWL AKA SAUTÉED BREAKFAST SALAD

A simple, delicious breakfast bowl (aka sautéed breakfast salad) with sautéed greens, roasted veggies and two fried eggs! You'll feel so good after starting your day with this combo of protein, healthy fat and veggies. Low carb, gluten-free and vegetarian.

A white bowl with sautéed greens, roasted cauliflower, two sunny side up eggs, avocado, microgreens and fresh dill.

Ready for one of the easiest breakfast recipes ever? This recipe was inspired by two things: my love of salads and my sweet

+ savory egg and oatmeal combo bowl. This bowl just has less grains and more greens!

A white bowl with sautéed greens, roasted cauliflower, two sunny side up eggs, avocado, microgreens and fresh dill.

I know some people think a salad for breakfast is weird, but in case you haven't noticed I'm attempting to change your mind. Previously I've posted a fall harvest breakfast salad and a blueberry breakfast salad, but today we're getting even more classic — a breakfast bowl with veggies and eggs!

Let's talk about why this breakfast salad recipe is so great:

It is super simple!

I love the combination of textures and flavors.

It reminds me of something you would find at a trendy brunch restaurant.

You start your day off with loads of veggies right off the bat! Hello energy!

You can check off your #saladeveryday... before noon.

You can make this recipe work for your taste buds. Like a particular green? Want a low carb breakfast — stick with low carb roasted veggies like cauliflower. Need more energy? Toss in some roasted sweet potatoes!

A white bowl with sautéed greens, roasted cauliflower, two sunny side up eggs, avocado, microgreens and fresh dill.

Just don't forget the dill! I've shared my love for dill on my Instagram stories but I have to make sure all of you know about my secret salad weapon. Are you a fan of dill? I feel like my child-hood consists of dill-packed potato salads and pickles which left a literal bad taste in my mouth.

And don't forget to snag some microgreens while you're at it — these babies are so nutrient dense and make salads look so pretty.

- Prep Time: 5 minutes
- Cook Time: 14 minutes

- Total Time: 19 minutes
- Yield: 1

This bowl is packed with sautéed greens, two fried eggs and roasted veggies! You'll feel so good after starting your day with this combo of protein and healthy fat.

Ingredients

- 2–3 teaspoons avocado or olive oil
- 2–3 eggs
- 1/4 cup chopped red onion
- 2 –3 cups baby greens (spinach, kale or your favorite green)
- 1/2 cup roasted cauliflower or roasted sweet potatoes
- 1/3 avocado, sliced
- microgreens
- fresh dill
- sea salt and pepper

Instructions

Heat 2 teaspoons oil in a large skillet over medium heat. Once hot add onion and sauté for about 5 minutes. Add greens and roasted cauliflower and toss to combine. Sprinkle with sea salt. Cook, stirring often, 2 minutes or just until greens begin to wilt.

Transfer veggies to a salad bowl and then crack two eggs into the same pan, adding a little more oil if needed. Cook eggs to desired consistency (I like mine sunny side up) sprinkle with salt and pepper and place on top of sautéed greens. Top bowl with microgreens, fresh dill and sliced avocado. Serve with more salt and pepper and hot sauce if desired.

NOTES

For roasted cauliflower/sweet potatoes: Spread 3-4 cups of chopped veggies on a large baking sheet (affiliate link) or stone and toss with 1-2 teaspoons avocado or olive oil, salt and pepper. Roast for 20 minutes at 425°F or until the veggies have browned and become tender. Be sure to toss the veggies at least once while roasting.

Nutrition

- Serving Size: 1 bowl w/ 2 eggs + cauliflower
- Calories: 370
- Sugar: 3g
- Fat: 29g
- Carbohydrates: 13g
- Fiber: 7g
- Protein: 17g

29

LOW CARB STIR FRY CAULIFLOWER RICE (VEGAN, GLUTEN FREE)

This superfood stir fry cauliflower rice is an easy way to turn your favorite seaweed sheets into a vitamin packed meal! Add some veggies and you're set!

Looking to get an extra boost of vitamins and minerals into your everyday meals? Well, I've got the recipe for you! I love it when I figure out **q**uick and easy ways to make healthy food ever healthier! The key is to keep it tasty, so you don't even know that it's extra good for you. This stir fry cauliflower rice is the perfect way to crush those healthy eating goals!

KIDS LOVE THESE SEAWEED SNACKS!

We eat their seaweed snacks every week, and I can't help but get excited that my kids willingly beg for something that's actually super healthy but feels like an unhealthy pre-packaged kid snack. They also have delicious seaweed chips in multiple flavors!

My favorite is the sriracha...mmmm. (Hint: if you click on the links above you can get a nice discount via amazon on their products until January 31! Stock up!) So when GimMe came to me again to create another recipe using their products I didn't even hesitate!

This go around, they wanted me to get creative and repurpose their seaweed sheets in a sneaky yet effective way. No. Problem. I knew I wanted it to be something easy because the ultimate combo when it comes to recipes is healthy but simple.

And this stir fry cauliflower rice hits the nail on the head! It's literally 5 simple steps and 9 easy ingredients to a meal so packed with flavor and nutrients you will wonder where it's been all your life! Oh and for those of you looking for something lower carb and low in calories and fat, yep. It's that too.

VITAMIN PACKED STIR FRY CAULIFLOWER RICE IN 5 EASY STEPS

Pulse seaweed sheets into small flakes

Pulse cauliflower into rice like pieces and chop veggies (Hint: you can buy pre-riced cauliflower and pre-chopped veggies for an even easier meal, SAY WHAT?!)

Saute ingredients

Mix in seaweed flakes

Devour...okay maybe this isn't really a step 😉

Viola! Dinner is served. I mean, does it get any better than easy, flavorful AND healthy? Nope. Not for this mom of 3. On your mark, get set, GO!

Superfood Stir Fry Cauliflower Rice in a blue bowl sitting on a wooden surface

If you're looking for a great pair for this low carb rice for an all around lower carb meal, try my Chinese Style Vegan Orange Cauliflower recipe!

- Prep Time: 10 mins
- Cook Time: 10 mins
- Total Time: 20 mins
- Servings: 2

Ingredients

- 7 full sheets GimMe Organic roasted seaweed
- 1 medium head cauliflower about 4 cups cauliflower rice if buying prepackaged
- 2 cups chopped mushrooms
- 2 cups chopped green onion
- 1 cup chopped red pepper
- ¼ cup Tamari or Soy Sauce
- 4 teaspoons finely chopped garlic
- 4 teaspoons sesame oil
- 4 teaspoons maple syrup

US Customary - Metric

Instructions

Place seaweed sheets into a food processor and pulse until they become small flakes. Make cauliflower rice by cutting head into pieces, cutting out most of the stem. Using a food processor pulse cauliflower until it is in small rice like pieces. You can also use a grater to grate the cauliflower if you do not have a processor.

Saute sesame oil and garlic in a large pan over medium heat until the garlic gets fragrant.

Add in the rest of the ingredients, except the seaweed flakes, and sauté while stirring until everything is cooked through and most of the liquid has evaporated. I prefer mine on the al dente side so taste as you go and remove from heat when you reach your desired consistency. Pour into a large bowl.

Add the desired amount of seaweed flakes to the bowl and mix well to incorporate. Serve as a main dish or as a side to any Asian inspired meal!

Recipe Notes

You can sub in any veggies you prefer in this. Add as many seaweed flakes as you want and save the rest to sprinkle on other meals!

Tips to prep ahead: Wash and chop veggies. Rice cauliflower. Grind seaweed into flakes. Baby/toddler food idea: Great kids meal!

Nutrition Facts

- Calories 283
- Calories from Fat 81
- Fat 9g14%
- Saturated Fat 1g5%
- Cholesterol 0mg0%
- Sodium 1140mg48%
- Potassium 1393mg40%
- Carbohydrates 44g15%
- Fiber 11g44%
- Sugar 20g22%
- Protein 10g20%
- Vitamin A 3330IU67%
- Vitamin C 141.6mg172%
- Calcium 135mg14%
- Iron 3.9mg22%

30

ZUCCHINI ROLLATINI

Zucchini Rollatini is a delicious, cheesy, veggie-loaded dish! Made with strips of grilled zucchini stuffed with a basil-cheese filling, then rolled and topped with marinara, mozzarella and baked in the oven until the cheese is hot and melted.

This cheesy, Zucchini Rollatini is a delicious, veggie-loaded dish! Made with strips of grilled zucchini stuffed with a basil-cheese filling, then rolled and topped with marinara, mozzarella and baked in the oven until the cheese is hot and melted.

Swapping pasta for zucchini in these roll ups make them low-carb and keto friendly. Zucchini is one of my favorite vegetables. If you need some zucchini inspiration you can see all my zucchini recipes here.

The inspiration for this dish came from my eggplant rollatini, one of my favorite summer meals. I modified that recipe a bit, keeping the cheese filling pretty simple and swapping the eggplant for zucchini.

To make the zucchini pliable, and to reduce liquid when they bake I grilled them on my grill pan before filling and rolling. This recipe was super easy and pretty *q*uick to whip up. The first time I tested these I baked them longer but I didn't like how watery they were. This time, I only baked them for 20 minutes and they came out perfect, not mushy or watery and the zucchini had the perfect texture – guys these came out SO good! This could be prepped ahead then baked when ready to eat.

Noodle-less Zucchini Rollatini is low-carb and delicious! Made with strips of grilled zucchini stuffed with a basil-cheese filling, then rolled and topped with marinara, mozzarella and baked in the oven until the cheese is hot and melted.

- Prep Time: 10 Mins
- Cook Time: 20 Mins
- Total Time: 30 Mins
- Yield:3 Servings

Ingredients

- 2 large, 14 oz each zucchini, cut lengthwise into 12 (1/4-inch thick) slices
- 1/2 teaspoon kosher salt
- fresh black pepper, to taste
- 1 cup *q*uick marinara sauce

- 1 large egg
- 2/3 cup part skim ricotta cheese, I like Polly-O
- 1/2 cup grated Pecorino Romano cheese, plus more for serving
- 1/4 cup chopped basil
- 1 garlic clove, minced
- 3/4 cup 3 oz shredded mozzarella (I like Polly-O)

Instructions

Preheat the oven to 400F. Spread 1/4 cup marinara sauce on the bottom of a 13 x 9-inch baking dish.

Cut the zucchini lengthwise, into 1/4-inch thick slices until you have a total of 12 slices about the same size. It's easiest to do this with a mandolin. My mandolin is from OXO.

Season both sides of the zucchini with 1/2 tsp salt and pepper, then grill on a grill pan over high heat to help dry out the zucchini, until pliable and grill marks form, but not fully cooked, about 2 minutes on each side.

In a medium bowl, beat the egg then mix together with ricotta, Pecorino Romano, basil, garlic, 1/8 tsp salt and 1/8 tsp pepper.

Spread the ricotta mixture (about 1 1/2 tablespoons each) evenly onto each zucchini slice, spreading to cover.

Roll up slices and arrange them each seam side down in the prepared dish. Top each with 1 tbsp marinara sauce and 1 tbsp mozzarella cheese and tightly cover with foil.

Bake 20 minutes, or until the cheese is hot and melted.

Nutrition facts

Serving: 4rolls, Calories: 318kcal, Carbohydrates: 18.5g, Protein: 21g, Fat: 17.5g, Saturated Fat: 10.5g, Cholesterol: 113mg, Sodium: 998mg, Fiber: 5g, Sugar: 9g

31

NO BAKE CHOCOLATE PEANUT BUTTER PROTEIN BARS

No bake chocolate peanut butter protein bars that taste just like a peanut butter cup. This low carb protein bar recipe will be your new favorite snack to keep in your fridge and enjoy all week long!

These chocolate peanut butter protein bars are easy to make because there's no baking required. All you need is an a pot or two, an 8×4 inch loaf pan, parchment paper and 7 simple ingredients:

- peanut butter: you can use whatever kind of nut butter you'd like, just make sure it's all natural (with no additives — just nuts + salt). I like Smucker's, Santa Cruz, Trader Joe's or Whole Foods natural creamy peanut butter.
- honey: this unrefined sweetener is perfect for holding together + sweetening the bars. If you are vegan, I suggest using coconut palm syrup or date syrup.
- coconut oil: you'll only need a tablespoon of coconut oil!
- vanilla extract: I'm such a vanilla lover, but if you find yourself out of vanilla, feel free to skip it!
- flaxseed meal: flaxseed meal is just ground flaxseeds! I absolutely LOVE how it adds fiber + protein to these bars. It does give the bar a nice toasty flavor too.
- protein powder: you can use plant based or a whey protein. My personal favorite is Vital Proteins collagen peptides (which is dairy free) but I also love aloha vanilla plant based protein powder for this recipe. Those are the two I highly recommend for flavor and consistency in this recipe.
- dark chocolate: you can use your favorite brand of dark chocolate. I recommend theo, divine or alter eco brands. Alter eco has a lot of great dairy free/vegan options!
- Optional: a little fancy sea salt for sprinkling on top.

These bars are seriously one of my favorite healthier treats to make because they're so freaking easy and do NOT require any baking. They also make an excellent post workout snack or late afternoon pick me up as they happen to pack 9g protein.

- Prep Time: 10 mins
- Cook Time: 30 mins
- Total Time: 40 mins

These bars are seriously one of my favorite healthier treats to make because they're so freaking easy and do NOT require any baking. They also make an excellent post workout snack or late afternoon pick me up as they happen to pack 9g protein.

No bake chocolate peanut butter protein bars that taste just like a peanut butter cup. This low carb, protein bar recipe will be your new favorite snack to keep in your fridge and enjoy all week long.

Ingredients

- ¾ cup natural creamy peanut butter (just peanuts + salt)
- ¼ cup honey (or coconut palm syrup, if vegan)
- 1 tablespoon melted coconut oil
- 1 teaspoon vanilla
- 1/3 cup ground flaxseed meal
- 1/2 cup of your favorite vanilla or plain protein powder*
- 2.5 ounces your favorite 85% dark chocolate bar
- Coarse sea salt for sprinkling on top

Instructions

In a medium bowl mix together peanut butter, honey, coconut oil, vanilla together until smooth. Add in ground flaxseed meal and protein powder of choice. Use a spoon to mix together until you can't anymore, then use clean hands to help work together. The batter should be similar to cookie dough.

Press into an 8x4 inch pan lined with parchment paper.

Make the chocolate layer by adding 2.5 ounces of dark chocolate to a small saucepan and melting until completely smooth. Pour the melted chocolate over the peanut butter layer and tilt the pan so that the chocolate covers the peanut butter layer entirely.

Place in the fridge for 30 minutes-1 hour before slicing into 10 bars or squares (either works but I love squares the most). Store covered in the fridge until ready to eat. Bars will keep for up to two weeks.

Recipe Notes

*Note: if the batter feels too dry, add ½ - 1 tablespoon of melted virgin coconut oil

For the protein powder: you can use plant based or a whey protein. My personal favorite is Vital Proteins collagen peptides (which is dairy free) but I also love aloha vanilla plant based protein powder for this recipe. Those are the two I highly recommend for flavor and consistency in this recipe.

Nutrition

- Servings: 10 bars
- Serving size: 1 protein bar
- Calories: 210kcal
- Fat: 13.8g
- Saturated fat: 3.4g
- Carbohydrates: 13.4g
- Fiber: 2.8g
- Sugar: 8g
- Protein: 8.6g

32

EASY CHOPPED AVOCADO CAPRESE SALAD RECIPE – CHERRY TOMATOES

The simplest, easy chopped Caprese salad recipe with 7 ingredients! Once you see how to make avocado Caprese salad with cherry tomatoes, you'll make this naturally healthy, keto salad over and over... and over.

Summer salads require two things: fresh flavors and minimal effort! And, low carb salads like this chopped Caprese salad with cherry tomatoes are meant to be enjoyed outside. This one passes the summer salad test. The flavors are light and refreshing, plus, you can make this avocado Caprese salad recipe with just 7 simple ingredients! Keto Caprese salad FTW!

I know a lot of people say that they get tired of eating salads, and that is what inspired me to create this avocado Caprese salad! There is nothing boring about these flavors, and the best part is that it's HEALTHY!

WHAT IS CAPRESE SALAD?

Caprese salad is an Italian style salad that has become pretty well known. Traditionally, chopped Caprese salad is full of fresh mozzarella cheese, tomatoes, and olive oil. It was invented in the 1950s because it's an amazing dish to make with fresh garden tomatoes.

CAPRESE SALAD INGREDIENTS

- Balsamic vinegar
- Olive oil
- Garlic powder
- Sea salt
- Black pepper
- Cherry or grape tomatoes
- Fresh mozzarella balls
- Avocado
- Fresh basil
- ingredients for caprese salad with cherry tomatoes

HOW TO MAKE CAPRESE SALAD

Ready to see how to make Caprese salad? It doesn't get any easier. We'll make the balsamic reduction first, then make up the salad.

In a small saucepan, add the balsamic vinegar. Simmer until the balsamic has thickened and reduced. This adds insane flavor, so don't skip the reduction step! You can also buy already reduced balsamic vinegar, but make sure that it doesn't have any added sweetener in it.

PRO TIP: The balsamic reduction will continue to thicken

after you remove it from the stove. So, you want to stop heating when it's a bit thinner than you think you'll need.

Make the dressing. Whisk together olive oil, garlic powder, sea salt, and black pepper.

Mix salad. Carefully toss in the tomatoes, mozzarella, avocado, and fresh basil.

Drizzle with balsamic reduction.

keto caprese salad mixed together

CAPRESE SALAD WITH CHERRY TOMATOES VARIATIONS

This is the best Caprese salad with balsamic already! But, here are some ideas if you want to make some additions:

Chicken − Dice up a grilled chicken breast and add to the avocado Caprese salad for some added protein. Sounds like the perfect summer lunch to me!

Bacon − No one says you have to be traditional all the time! Cook up some bacon in the oven, crumble it, and toss it in.

Olives − They add a nice tangy flavor to the chopped Caprese salad.

No, you don't have to use balsamic vinegar in keto Caprese salad. The original Caprese salad recipe didn't call for balsamic vinegar at all, just a drizzle of olive oil.

So, if you don't love balsamic, it's okay to leave it out. I think it adds amazing flavor and depth, but you can make adjustments to meet your needs.

IS CAPRESE SALAD HEALTHY?

Yes, chopped Caprese salad is very healthy! This Caprese salad with cherry tomatoes is loaded with vegetables and protein, zinc, vitamin B12, beta-carotene, potassium, and more.

Enjoy this avocado Caprese salad as an appetizer or main dish because you will be getting lots of nutrient-rich ingredients.

HOW DO YOU STORE KETO CAPRESE SALAD?

Store Caprese salad with cherry tomatoes in an airtight container in the fridge. It will last 2-3 days if it's properly stored and makes wonderful leftovers.

This is the best Caprese salad recipe because you can also make it ahead for meal planning.

- Whisk – I love this utensil set because they are all super easy to clean and use. Plus, they have bamboo handles.
- Spoon Rest – It's not required, but having a spoon rest sure helps keep the kitchen organized and clean. Worth it!
- Serving Bowl – This set of serving bowls are amazing because you can bake in them, serve food in them, or mix ingredients. They are practically the only bowls you need.

The simplest, easy chopped Caprese salad recipe with 7 ingredients! Once you see how to make avocado Caprese salad with cherry tomatoes, you'll make this naturally healthy, keto salad over and over... and over.

- Prep Time 10 minutes
- Cook Time 10 minutes
- Total Time 20 minutes
- Servings: 4

Ingredients

- 1 cup Balsamic vinegar
- 1/4 cup Extra virgin olive oil
- 1/4 tsp Garlic powder
- 1/4 tsp Sea salt
- 1/8 tsp Black pepper
- 2 cups Grape tomatoes (halved; measured after slicing)
- 1 cup Fresh mozzarella balls
- 1 medium Avocado (diced)
- 1/3 cup Fresh basil (chopped)
- Wholesome Yum Keto Sweeteners

Instructions

Pour the balsamic vinegar into a very small saucepan. Heat over medium-low heat for about 10-15 minutes, keeping it at a low simmer but not boiling. Simmer until slightly thickened but still pourable, and volume has reduced to about 1/3 cup. (This is balsamic reduction - it will thicken as it cools, so don't let it thicken too much when hot.)

When the balsamic reduction is ready, let it cool to room temperature.

Meanwhile, in a large bowl, whisk together the olive oil, garlic powder, sea salt, and black pepper.

Add the tomatoes, mozzarella, avocado, and fresh basil. Toss to coat. Drizzle the entire salad with 1 tablespoon balsamic reduction. (You can save the rest for another use.)

Avocado tuna salad in a bowl

Paleo Whole30 Chicken Salad with Avocado Recipe - An easy paleo whole30 chicken salad recipe with avocado - only 5 ingredients! Plus, simple ideas for serving chicken avocado salad with lime and cilantro.

Nutrition Facts

- Calories284
- Fat26g
- Protein6g
- Total Carbs8g
- Net Carbs4g
- Fiber4g
- Sugar3g

33

COLORFUL RAINBOW SALAD RECIPE + POMEGRANATE VINAIGRETTE DRESSING

Learn how to make this HEALTHY colorful rainbow salad recipe with pomegranate vinaigrette dressing. It's so EASY and just 10 ingredients!

This colorful rainbow salad recipe with pomegranate vinaigrette dressing is not only a beautiful salad, but it's also a great way to incorporate a variety of fruits and veggies all in one bowl! And did I mention it's only 10 ingredients – pomegranate vinaigrette included?

Whenever I over-hear people saying that healthy food is

boring, or too complicated, or too time-consuming, I want to show them a picture of this salad! And tell them how delicious it is! And then go on and on about how easy and simple it is to make. Because there is absolutely nothing boring or complicated in this colorful salad. It's bright, beautiful, nutritious, and mighty delicious. The rainbow of colors along with the accompanying flavors are sure to brighten up any cloudy day – or any meal that needs a little something. 😊

It's got all of the flavors and textures you need in a dish: sweet and salty; creamy and crunchy; rich and acidic. When you need an exciting salad (and who doesn't?!), this is a great one to serve with just about anything. Be sure to let me know what you think with a rating below, or if you swap out any of the ingredients for another fruit or vegetable. Can't wait to hear what you think about it. My guess is that you'll love it as much as we do.

WHAT IS RAINBOW SALAD?

Rainbow salad is just what you might think it is! It's a colorful salad with lots of fruits and veggies. In my rainbow veggie salad, I've included a wide array of hues – red, orange, yellow, light and dark greens, purple. This colorful salad is sure to make a beautiful addition to any meal.

Rainbow Salad Ingredients:

- pomegranate arils
- sweet bell peppers
- crisp spinach
- creamy avocado

HOW TO MAKE COLORFUL RAINBOW SALAD

When you're looking for veggie salad ideas, this 10-ingredient salad with pomegranate vinaigrette dressing should be your top choice. Let me show you how easy it is to make!

First we will make the pomegranate balsamic vinaigrette. It's quick and easy.

Then we'll prep our vegetables.

Next we toss the spinach with the dressing. This ensures that each bite of salad has a nice coating of dressing on it.

When the spinach is dressed, it's time to top this colorful rainbow salad with the peppers, cabbage, pomegranate arils, avocado, and toasted pumpkin seeds for crunch. You can drizzle with extra salad dressing if desired.

HOW TO MAKE POMEGRANATE VINAIGRETTE DRESSING

This pomegranate salad dressing has just the right amount of natural sweetness, but is still quite low in sugar and carbs. All you need to do is combine all of the ingredients in a jar or bottle, and shake until emulsified.

The dressing doesn't require any chopping or cutting, so it can be made in about two minutes! I prefer to make my own dressings because I think they taste much better than store-bought versions but also because the ingredients are so much healthier.

CAN YOU MAKE RAINBOW SALAD AHEAD?

You can definitely make parts of the rainbow salad ahead but you wouldn't want to dress the greens or put anything together until right before serving.

If you'd like to make some of the components ahead of time, I would recommend:

Mixing up the dressing. This can be stored in the fridge for a week or two. If the oil solidifies, simply take it out of the refrigerator 30 minutes before serving to let it come to room temperature. Or, run the bottle under warm water.

Removing pomegranate arils. If you are buying a whole pomegranate, you'll need to remove the arils. This can be done by cutting the pomegranate in half and then lightly tapping the skin of it over a bowl so that the arils fall into the bowl.

Slicing cabbage. Cabbage can be thinly sliced and stored in the fridge for 2-4 days.

Toasting the nuts. If you're nuts are raw, toast them in a hot skillet, until golden brown and fragrant, about 2-5 minutes. These can be stored in an airtight container at room temperature.

- Salad Dressing Shaker – I use this for all of my salad recipes as the dressing shaker is super convenient, easy to store, and requires less cleanup. You can place it on the table for a family meal, so each person can decide how much dressing they want, and use the same container for storing any leftovers.
- Glass Bowl Set – These nesting bowls can be used for both prepping and serving raw vegetable salads like this one.
- Wooden Salad Tongs – Your colorful salad recipe needs tongs that are just as beautiful!

This HEALTHY colorful rainbow salad recipe with pomegranate vinaigrette dressing is so EASY and just 10 ingredients!

- Prep Time 10 minutes
- Total Time 10 minutes
- Servings: 6

Ingredients

- Salad
- 4 cups Spinach
- 1 medium Bell pepper (chopped) *
- 1/2 medium Avocado (cubed)
- 1/2 cup Red cabbage (shredded)
- 1/2 cup Pomegranate arils
- 1/4 cup Pumpkin seeds (preferably roasted)
- Pomegranate balsamic vinaigrette dressing
- 3 tbsp Olive oil
- 1 tbsp Pomegranate juice
- 1/2 tbsp Balsamic vinegar
- 1/4 tsp Garlic salt
- Black pepper (to taste - optional)
- Wholesome Yum Keto Sweeteners

Instructions

Place all dressing ingredients into a jar or airtight container. Shake vigorously until emulsified.

Toss the dressing with spinach until evenly distributed. Add remaining ingredients and toss again to combine.

Cauliflower Potato Salad Recipe (Low Carb Paleo Potato Salad) - This easy cauliflower mock potato salad recipe is low carb, keto, paleo, gluten-free, whole 30, and healthy. It's a crowd pleaser for everyone, too!

This Japanese kani salad recipe with real crab meat takes just 10 minutes to whip up. Healthy, creamy, and delicious! Low carb, paleo, and gluten-free, too.

This easy chicken salad recipe is packed with flavorful herbs. Learn how to make simple, healthy chicken salad in just a few minutes!

cucumber avocado salad overhead shot

Nutrition Facts

- Calories138
- Fat12g
- Protein3g
- Total Carbs7g
- Net Carbs4g
- Fiber3g
- Sugar3g

34

EASY ITALIAN KETO LOW CARB ZUCCHINI FRITTERS RECIPE

Just 6 ingredients to make this low carb zucchini fritters recipe! These easy Italian zucchini fritters are keto friendly AND family friendly.

Head to the garden and gather your zucchini for this delicious, low carb zucchini fritters recipe! Easy zucchini fritters are ready in less than 15 minutes, and take just 6 ingredients. Follow my tips for perfect Italian zucchini fritters every time.

And did I mention they are healthy? My zucchini fritters keto are low carb, gluten-free, and full of veggies.

I'm all about easy zucchini recipes this time of year, and these keto zucchini fritters are such a fun way to enjoy my favorite squash ever. They freeze well too, so if your garden is exploding with fresh zucchini, make these gluten free zucchini fritters and freeze them to enjoy later.

The best zucchini fritters are crispy and golden brown on the outside, soft and creamy on the inside, and perfect with a dollop of sour cream. When are you going to make them?

They are very similar, but zucchini fritters are a bit more dense, while zucchini pancakes are lighter and fluffier. And, pancakes use flour (almond flour for my low carb ones!), while fritters use no flour at all.

HOW TO MAKE ZUCCHINI FRITTERS

This low carb zucchini fritters recipe is so easy to make!

Drain the zucchini. This is an important step that you don't want to skip! Once you have your shredded zucchini in a colander, sprinkle with salt and let it sit over the sink for 10 minutes. The salt helps to draw excess water out of the zucchini so that your keto zucchini fritters and nice and crispy!

Wring out zucchini. Part two of removing water from the zucchini is to then wrap the zucchini in a kitchen towel and squeeze out as much water as you can.

Mix zucchini fritter batter. Place the zucchini in a large bowl, and add the grated parmesan cheese, eggs, Italian seasoning, and garlic. Mix together.

Shape the zucchini fritters. Scoop out a tablespoon of the fritter batter and flatten it into a disc shape with your fingers.

Fry up the low carb zucchini fritters. Heat a large skillet over medium-high heat, add some oil to the pan and then fry the keto fritters for about 2 minutes per side, until golden brown.

WHY ARE MY FRITTERS SOGGY?

If your fried zucchini fritters are soggy, it's probably because you didn't remove enough water from the zucchini.

Zucchini have a ton of water, and if you don't remove enough, the middle of the fritters will seem soggy.

Steps one and two in my recipe are especially important.

Letting the shredded zucchini sit with salt helps draw water out, and then squeezing the shredded zucchini with a towel ensures that you get rid of as much water as you can.

ARE ZUCCHINI FRITTERS HEALTHY?

Yes! Zucchini fritters are healthy. These low carb zucchini fritters are keto-friendly, gluten-free, and packed with vegetables.

HOW MANY CALORIES IN ZUCCHINI FRITTERS?

In this zucchini fritters recipe, 4 fritters have 127 calories. You'll find all of the nutrition stats below in the recipe card.

CAN YOU MAKE LOW CARB ZUCCHINI FRITTERS AHEAD?

You can make these Italian zucchini fritters ahead of time. Because they are fried, I do think they are best freshly fried and served hot out of the fry pan...

...but, if you need to make them ahead, you can simply reheat them when you're ready to eat in a hot skillet (preferred) or 375 degrees F oven on a baking sheet.

CAN YOU FREEZE ZUCCHINI FRITTERS?

Yes! You can freeze these keto zucchini fritters.

The best way to freeze the fritters is to freeze them on a sheet pan in a single layer. Once they are frozen solid, you can transfer them to a zip lock bag.

When you're ready to eat, bake them at 375 degrees F, until they are hot all the way through.

- 14-Cup Food Processor – Quick zucchini fritters are even quicker when you shred the zucchini with the food processor.
- Medium Cookie Scoop – Using a cookie scoop will help get the correct amount of Italian zucchini fritters batter each time!
- Ceramic Nonstick Chef Pan – I like how evenly these heat up. Perfect for frying zucchini fritters!

Just 6 ingredients to make this low carb zucchini fritters recipe! These easy Italian zucchini fritters are keto friendly AND family friendly.

- Prep Time 15 minutes
- Cook Time 20 minutes
- Total Time 35 minutes
- Servings: 6

Ingredients

- 8 cups Zucchini (grated, loose in the measuring cup; ~ 8 medium zucchini)
- 1 tsp Sea salt
- 1 cup Grated parmesan cheese
- 2 large Eggs
- 2 tsp Italian seasoning
- 4 cloves Garlic (minced)
- Olive oil (for frying)
- Wholesome Yum Keto Sweeteners

Instructions

Place the zucchini and salt into a large collander and mix together. Drain over the sink for 10 minutes.

Wrap the zucchini in a kitchen towel. Squeeze and twist over the sink to drain as much water as possible.

Place the zucchini into a large bowl. Add remaining ingredients and stir together.

Heat a generous amount of olive oil in a large skillet over medium-high heat, for about 2 minutes. Spoon rounded tablespoonfuls (28 grams) of the batter onto the skillet and flatten to about 1/4 to 1/3 inch thick. Fry for about 2 minutes on each side, until golden brown.

Serve with sour cream and parsley.

Low Carb Keto Zucchini Lasagna Recipe with Meat & Pesto - No Noodles - Delicious low carb keto zucchini lasagna with meat

& pesto! This easy zucchini lasagna recipe includes lots of TIPS, plus freezing & make ahead instructions. No noodles needed!

9-Ingredient Spaghetti S*q*uash Carbonara (Low Carb, Gluten-free) - This low carb, gluten-free spaghetti squash recipe features a creamy, decadent bacon carbonara sauce. Only 9 ingredients and 9 grams carbs!

Low Carb Hamburger Buns Recipe (Keto, Paleo) - There's no need to settle for a bun-less burger on a keto diet. It's easy to make your own low carb hamburger buns for all your summer cookouts!

This gluten-free, paleo, low carb meatloaf recipe is super easy to make. You need only 8 ingredients and 10 minutes prep time!

Nutrition Facts

- Calories127
- Fat6g
- Protein10g
- Total Carbs6g
- Net Carbs5g
- Fiber1g
- Sugar4g

35

STRAWBERRY DOLE WHIP RECIPE

If you've never tried Disney's Dole Whip before, you are in for a real treat!

- Total Time: 5 minutes
- Yield: 4 - 5 servings

Ingredients

- 1 cup sliced frozen strawberries (120g)
- 1 cup frozen raspberries, or additional strawberries
- 1/4 cup milk of choice or canned coconut milk
- 1 1/2 tsp sugar or sweetener of choice, or pinch uncut stevia
- 2 tsp lemon juice
- 1/16 tsp salt

Instructions

Strawberry Dole Whip Recipe: Combine all ingredients in a blender and blend until smooth. Scoop out and eat OR put in a plastic bag and freeze ten minutes, then cut a hole in the bag's edge and squeeze out in a swirl. (Or you can use a Yonanas machine if you have one – I used the bag method.) The addition of lemon might sound strange, but it really makes the recipe!

Nutrition facts

- Calories 17
- Calories from fat 2
- Total fat 0.3g
- Trans fat 0.0g
- Cholesterol 0mg
- Sodium 49mg
- Pottasium 77mg
- Total carbohydrates 3.8g
- Dietary fiber 1.0g
- Sugars 2.4g
- Protein 0.4g

36

ZUCCHINI ALFREDO RECIPE (KETO ZOODLES ALFREDO)

Keto zucchini noodles Alfredo (keto zoodles) has a rich, creamy sauce that's low carb & gluten-free. It's the best zucchini Alfredo ever!

Zucchini season is here, zucchini season is here! Can you just imagine me shouting this from a rooftop? That's what I feel like doing right now because that also means it's zucchini Alfredo season. And that is is one of the best times of the year, don't you think? Keto zucchini noodles alfredo is the meal you'll want to make over and over again. It's a classic for a reason! And so much easier to make at home than you might think. Once you spiralize your keto zoodles, you'll whip up your quick Alfredo sauce to drizzle over the top. And I'm sharing even more keto zoodle recipes below, because I know you'll want to try them all during zucchini season!

My absolute favorite use of zucchini is zucchini noodles, keto zoodle spaghetti, or zoodles – there are so many different names!

Place your zucchini in a spiralizer, give the handle a few cranks around, and voila – you've got gorgeous, delicious zucchini noodles. The first time I tried it (years ago), I couldn't believe how easy it was. You can also use a julienne peeler to create zucchini noodles manually, if that's what you have.

Either way, if you're missing pasta, zoodles are your perfect solution. And, my zucchini noodles recipe will make it super easy for you.

The zucchini noodles are the star of these zucchini pasta with Alfredo sauce, keeping the dish light, colorful, and delicious. For as long as I can get my hands on good zucchini, I'll be making zoodles Alfredo all summer long – and well into fall.

HOW TO MAKE ZUCCHINI ALFREDO

Ready to see how to make zucchini Alfredo? It's super simple:

Prep the zoodles. I have a whole guide about how to make zucchini noodles here, which goes into many different preparation methods and which ones I think are best. Be sure to check it out if you love zucchini noodles.

Make the Alfredo sauce. In a skillet, you'll cook together butter, garlic, almond milk, heavy cream, and nutmeg. Then you'll whisk in the arrowroot powder and Parmesan cheese. The small amount of arrowroot powder is the key to thickening the sauce without flour (though you can also use xanthan gum instead, to further reduce carbs if that is a priority). Alternatively, if you don't need the Alfredo sauce to be lightened up on calories, you can make a classic keto Alfredo sauce like this. It's a bit heavier, but low in carbs.

Cook the keto zucchini noodles. In a hot skillet, stir fry until barely softened, but still crunchy.

TIP: Make sure you don't over cook the zoodles. We want them crunchy, not soggy!

Toss the zoodles with the Alfredo. Zucchini pasta Alfredo is ready to eat!

TIP: Serve the zoodles Alfredo right away. It can get watery if it sits.

WHAT IS THE TEXTURE OF ZOODLES?

The texture of zoodles can vary greatly. It all depends on how they are prepared. I recommend cooking them lightly and quickly so they don't get too soggy.

Raw zoodles have a crunch similar to cucumber, but lightly cooked they are a little softer and more tender.

IS ALFREDO SAUCE HEALTHY?

Alfredo sauce can be healthy! This zucchini noodle Alfredo is made with just 7 simple ingredients – no weird fillers or gums like some of the store-bought versions. One of the reasons I love to make my own food is because I know exactly what goes into my recipes.

HOW TO STORE ZUCCHINI NOODLES ALFREDO

Zucchini noodles are best served fresh! I would recommend making the amount you will eat, or prepping the zoodles and making the sauce ahead of time.

You can spiralize them in advance and keep them in the fridge uncooked. Then, when you're ready to cook, pat them dry first.

Cooking zoodles ahead of time is also not recommended, but if you must, do not mix them with sauce until ready to serve. They will continue to release water after cooking, so pat them dry again before adding sauce and serving.

CAN YOU FREEZE KETO ZOODLES?

No! Do not freeze keto zoodles. I repeat, do not freeze keto zoodles. Do not freeze zoodles. Trust me, I've tried and my attempts resulted in a watery mess and weird texture.

WHAT TO SERVE WITH KETO ZUCCHINI NOODLES ALFREDO

This zucchini noodles Alfredo doesn't need much, but I do like to add a protein to it so that it's a filling meal. It can be as simple as:

- Grilled chicken or shrimp
- Juicy baked chicken breast
- Tuscan garlic chicken
- Crispy chicken thighs
- Sirloin steak

Tabletop Spiralizer – If you plan on making lots of keto zucchini pasta recipes, you'll want the tabletop spiralizer. I love this version because it attaches to the counter to prevent slipping.

Handheld Spiralizer – Another great option for spiralizing keto zucchini noodles recipes.

Microplane Zester – I love using this for the garlic in my creamy zucchini noodles sauce – it ensures that there aren't any big clumps of garlic!

Keto zucchini noodles Alfredo (keto zoodles) has a rich, creamy sauce that's low carb & gluten-free. It's the best zucchini Alfredo ever!

- Prep Time 10 minutes
- Cook Time 15 minutes
- Total Time 25 minutes
- Servings: 4

Ingredients

- 3 medium Zucchini
- 1 tsp Butter
- 2 cloves Garlic (minced)
- 1/4 tsp Nutmeg (or 1/2 tsp if you like a stronger nutmeg flavor)

- 1/2 cup Unsweetened almond milk
- 1/3 cup Heavy cream
- 3/4 cup Grated parmesan cheese
- 1 tbsp Arrowroot powder (*see notes for alternative)
- Black pepper
- Wholesome Yum Keto Sweeteners

Instructions

Make zucchini noodles using a spiralizer or julienne peeler.

Melt the butter in another skillet over medium heat. Add garlic and cook about one minute, until soft and fragrant.

Reduce heat to medium-low. Stir in the almond milk, heavy cream, and nutmeg. Bring to a gentle simmer.

In a small bowl, whisk the arrowroot powder with just enough water to dissolve it (1-2 tablespoons (15-30 mL)), until smooth with no lumps. Whisk the mixture into the sauce on the stove. Whisk in the parmesan cheese. Add black pepper to taste. Continue to heat, stirring constantly, until the cheese is melted and the sauce starts to thicken. Remove the sauce from the pan, cover, and set aside.

Pat the zucchini noodles dry with paper towels. Add the zucchini noodles to the pan and turn up the heat to medium-high. Stir fry until barely softened but still crunchy, about 2-4 minutes. Stir in the sauce. Garnish with fresh parsley and additional parmesan cheese if desired.

Baked Easy Cheesy Zucchini Casserole Recipe (Zucchini Gratin) - This easy zucchini gratin recipe is a baked cheesy zucchini casserole that everyone will love! Healthy, low carb, gluten-free, and delicious. Only 10 minutes prep time & simple ingredients!

Easy Healthy Pan Fried Squash and Zucchini Recipe - This easy pan fried squash recipe (or fried zucchini recipe) is crispy & delicious. Learn how to make fried squash and zucchini the healthy way! Naturally low carb and gluten-free.

Nutrition Facts

- Calories209

- Fat16g
- Protein11g
- Total Carbs9g
- Net Carbs7g
- Fiber2g
- Sugar3g

LOW CARB SPAGHETTI SQUASH BOWLS

Getting those extra veggies in with these low carb spaghetti squash bowls loaded with all the things! Customizable and the perfect family meal.

I never thought veggie noodles could taste so good! It's all in the toppings. From ultra rich vegan cream sauce, to marinara and sautéed mushrooms, this dinner will win the entire family over.

HOW DO YOU CUT A SPAGHETTI SQUASH?

Believe it or not, there is a right way to cut a spaghetti squash so you get the most out of those noodles.

The strands of a spaghetti squash run circular around the squash width wise. Many people, including me many moons ago before I got with it, cut their squash length wise.

If you do this, you are chopping those strands into shorter pieces. Also, you aren't giving the inside room to let the moisture escape, resulting in a mushier end product. And you know how I feel about much (barf).

So you should always cut your squash into a bowl versus a boat.

Also, to allow the most moisture to escape while roasting, so you don't get that barflike mush factor, cut the ends of as well for ventilation.

HOW DO YOU COOK A SPAGHETTI SQUASH?

So once you have cut your spaghetti squash correctly, you want to cook it so that it doesn't get mushy. At least if you want this to be one of the best low carb spaghetti alternatives ever.

Here are the steps I follow, with an optional fancy extra trick:

- Cut ends off of the spaghetti squash.
- Cut it in half width wise to get 2 bowl like pieces, you can also cut it multiple times to get smaller ring like pieces.
- Scrape out the seeds in the middle.
- If you want to get fancy, salt your pieces and allow them to sit so that some of the moisture is drawn out (much like you would do to zucchini), then wipe dry. I have skipped this step many times and still gotten an amazing end result.
- Drizzle with a touch of oil, if you use it and if not just rub with a bit of broth, and salt if you did not do step 4.
- Place on a parchment lined cookie sheet and bake at 400 for about 30-40 minutes, you want the sides of the squash to just slightly push in. If you do this

right, you can scrape out perfect spaghetti like
strands!
- Collage of raw spaghetti squash on a pan cut in half
and with seeds taken out.

ARE THERE OTHER WAYS TO COOK A SPAGHETTI SQUASH?

Roasting in the oven is my favorite was to cook all my
vegetables. It brings out the best flavor, especially with things like
spaghetti squash which can otherwise be bland.

However, there are many other ways you can cook it if you
prefer. I have not tried these, so you will need to experiment, but
here is a rough idea:

- In the crockpot: cook on high for 3-4 hours or low for
6-7
- In the Instant Pot: cook on manual for about 15
minutes
- In the microwave: cook for about 8-10 minutes

WHAT GOES INTO SPAGHETTI SQUASH BOWLS?

My favorite thing about this dinner is that it is SO
customizable. I have less tantrums which makes me a more
pleasant person.

I set up the toppings like a taco bar, because if I can mention
tacos I will, and the kids go down and add whatever they want.

The best part is that because they are getting veggies in even if
they simply eat it plain or with a touch of my favorite Grateable
Vegan Parmesan, they are still getting a healthy meal!

But for the rest of us that like to indulge, the toppings are
endless! Here are some of our favorites:

- Ultra rich vegan cream sauce (I have so many versions
like the cream sauces from my vegan scalloped

cauliflower, vegan orzo risotto or vegan sharp white cheese sauce)
- Pesto (So many pestos, so little s*q*uash. Try the pesto from my pesto pasta salad, broccoli spinach pesto, spinach tahini pesto or kale arugula pesto!)
- Marinara (There are a bunch of versions on here, some of our favorites are my easy fresh tomato marinara, raw marinara sauce and crockpot marinara)
- Sautéed mushrooms
- Crumbled vegan sausage or my homemade chickpea sausage crumbles
- Grateable Vegan Parmesan Cheese
- Baked spaghetti s*q*uash half with fork in it surrounded by toppings

CAN I MAKE THE BOWLS AHEAD OF TIME?

Another great thing about this recipe, as if I haven't already sold you, is that you can make everything you need ahead of time. It's a meal planners dream!

You can definitely roast the spaghetti squash ahead of time. I leave it intact, meaning I don't fork out the spaghetti, then store in an airtight container. When I'm ready, I heat it in the microwave or oven.

Baked spaghetti s*q*uash half being topped with mushrooms, marinara and pesto

All of the toppings can easily be made the weekend before too, you can even batch prep and make doubles of some to use with another meal! Here are some of my suggestions for each topping:

Marinara:

- Vegan Beanball Subs
- 3 Ingredient Spinach Tomato Pasta Sauce
- Easy Vegan Vegetable Lasagna
- Zucchini Ravioli
- Creamy Pesto and Sausage Lasagna

- Pizza Burrito

Pesto:

- Easy Vegan Vegetable Lasagna
- Creamy Pesto and Sausage Lasagna
- Pesto Pasta Salad
- Broccoli Pesto Pasta
- Pasta Bake with Sun-Dried Tomatoes and Pesto

Vegan Cream Sauce:

- Scalloped Cauliflower
- Creamy Orzo Risotto
- Easy Vegan Vegetable Lasagna
- Creamy Pesto and Sausage Lasagna
- Zucchini Ravioli
- Pizza Burrito

Getting those extra veggies in with these low carb spaghetti squash bowls loaded with all the things! Customizable and the perfect family meal.

- Prep Time: 30 mins
- Cook Time: 1 hr
- Total Time: 1 hr 30 mins

Ingredients

- 2 medium spaghetti squash
- 1 cup Fresh tomato marinara
- 1 cup Cream sauce
- 1 cup Chickpea vegan sausage crumbles or store bought vegan sausage
- 1 cup Broccoli spinach pesto
- Grateable Vegan Parmesan

- 2 cups sliced mushrooms
- 1/4 teaspoon sea salt
- oil or broth to sauté
- US Customary - Metric

Instructions

Preheat oven to 400.

Cut the ends off of the spaghetti squash and then cut in half widthwise (see post).

Scrape out seeds, an ice cream scooper makes a great tool for scraping.

Optional: salt the spaghetti squash pieces to allow some of the moisture to drain out. Wipe down with a paper towel.

Brush with oil or veggie broth and salt (if you didn't salt them already).

Place on parchment lined cookie sheet. Bake for 30-40 minutes or until skin is soft to the touch.

While the spaghetti squash is baking, make the rest of your toppings if you haven't already.

To make the mushrooms, sauté with oil/broth and salt until all of the liquid has evaporated.

Once spaghetti squash is done, take them out of the oven and use a fork to scrape the insides to get the "spaghetti" noodles. Keep the "spaghetti" inside the squash bowl.

Top each spaghetti bowl with toppings of choice.

If you want, you can put them back in the oven and bake for another 5-10 minutes. Enjoy!

Recipe Notes

Make it easy with store bought toppings!

Add or take away any other toppings you prefer!

Nutrition Facts

- Calories 515
- Calories from Fat 225

- Fat 25g38%
- Saturated Fat 1g5%
- Trans Fat 0g
- Polyunsaturated Fat 0g
- Monounsaturated Fat 0g
- Cholesterol 0mg0%
- Sodium 1005mg42%
- Potassium 955mg27%
- Carbohydrates 57g19%
- Fiber 12g48%
- Sugar 17g19%
- Protein 15g30%
- Vitamin A 670IU13%
- Vitamin C 18.2mg22%
- Calcium 156mg16%
- Iron 4.7mg26%